THE
TRAIN LOVER'S

PUZZLE BOOK

200 BRAIN-TEASING
ACTIVITIES

THE TRAIN LOVER'S PUZZLE BOOK

An Hachette UK Company
www.hachette.co.uk

Summersdale Publishers Ltd
Part of Octopus Publishing Group Limited
Carmelite House
50 Victoria Embankment
LONDON
EC4Y 0DZ
UK

www.summersdale.com

Printed and bound in Poland

ISBN: 978-1-80007-188-9

Substantial discounts on bulk quantities of Summersdale books are available to corporations, professional associations and other organizations. For details contact general enquiries by telephone: +44 (0) 1243 771107 or email: enquiries@summersdale.com

THE
TRAIN LOVER'S
· PUZZLE BOOK ·

200 BRAIN-TEASING
ACTIVITIES

NEIL SOMERVILLE

summersdale

*This book is dedicated to you
and to everyone involved
in the railways.*

Thank you.

INTRODUCTION

There is something special about trains. With their power, speed and comfort they can take us to where we need to go, carry vast quantities of freight or, if travelling on a heritage line, remind us of another era.

Trains can also have personal significance. Perhaps you remember taking a particular journey, meeting or seeing someone off or being whisked away on holiday on the rails?

This book helps celebrate the specialness of trains, but in a different way. In the pages that follow are all sorts of train-related puzzles, ranging from mystery sudokus and word searches, to coded crosswords and trivia, as well as questions that will have you pondering some strange-but-true scenarios. The puzzles are for all, whether you're a train aficionado or someone with a simple fondness, there is much variety here that covers all eras.

I hope *The Train Lover's Puzzle Book* will entertain, surprise and hold many delights. Welcome aboard, enjoy the ride and have fun.

Neil Somerville

ANAGRAMS

Unscramble the following to reveal items and features often seen in a railway station.

1. ITEM AT CHECK-IN

2. RARE RIB

3. I GO INTO WARM

4. IF GOT BORED

5. A REAL COST

MYSTERY SUDOKU

Complete the grid so that every row, column and 3 × 3 box contains the letters AEGHILSTW in any order. One row or column contains a seven-letter word which describes something that plays an important part in the running of the railways. What is it?

	G				E			L
	L		G	A				I
	S					T		
	I			H				A
		T	L		A	I		
H				W			L	
		G					I	
A				I	G		H	
W			S				A	

RAILWAY SLANG

There are many slang words used on the railways, but what do the following mean?

1. RABBITS
a) Track maintenance workers
b) Short-distance travellers
c) Slow or local trains

2. DODGER
a) Shunting truck
b) Train with a locomotive at each end
c) Heavy freight train

3. TUB
a) Turntable
b) Tank engine
c) Brake

4. MIKE
a) Foreman
b) Shunting-yard engine
c) Reversing lever of a steam locomotive

DOWN WORD

Place a three-letter word in the spaces in each row to complete a six-letter word. When the grid is completed correctly, a new word in the shaded letters will be formed. This is an important and necessary part of the railways. What is it?

			O	R	E
			A	C	A
			S	I	T
			E	O	R
			R	K	S
			T	L	E
			H	E	R

WORD SEARCH

Find all the following London Underground stations in the word search and in the remaining squares you will discover another station. What is it?

Angel

Balham

Barking

East Ham

Epping

Euston

Leyton

Northolt

Oval

Paddington

Pinner

Poplar

Richmond

Royal Oak

Ruislip

Temple

West Acton

S	P	N	N	B	A	R	K	I	N	G
L	O	A	O	O	A	N	U	T	H	W
A	K	M	D	T	R	L	G	K	E	E
V	R	A	N	D	S	T	H	E	S	S
O	I	H	O	P	I	U	H	A	L	T
P	C	T	R	L	I	N	E	O	M	A
I	H	S	E	A	A	L	G	I	L	C
N	M	A	N	M	L	Y	S	T	G	T
N	O	E	T	O	P	P	O	I	O	O
E	N	O	T	Y	E	L	O	R	U	N
R	D	G	N	I	P	P	E	P	N	R

STRANGE BUT TRUE

On 23 May 1920, the French President Paul Deschanel caught a train, but what was to go wrong?

1. As he was travelling on official business, he did not buy a ticket. When a guard asked for his ticket and the president did not have one, the guard insisted he accompany him to the guard's van. Only then was the guard prepared to look at documents the president showed him to verify who he was.

2. The president had taken some sleeping pills and, feeling hot, leaned out of an open window. Probably due to the medication, he lost his balance and fell off the train.

3. It was late at night and the president was in a rush. As he got to the station and saw a train was about to depart, he quickly got on board. However, this particular train had finished for the day and was being taken to a siding. The president ended up locked in the train and parked in a siding until the following morning.

4. The president was travelling late at night and knew the train would arrive at his destination at 0.45 a.m. the following morning. When the train stopped at 0.45 a.m., the president got off and found himself standing on the edge of a field, unable to reboard the train. The train had stopped at a signal with the president miles from the nearest settlement.

CODED CROSSWORD

In the grid below, each letter of the alphabet has been replaced by a number. To solve the puzzle, you must decide which letter is represented by which number. To help you start, one of the words has been partly filled in. When you have solved the code, complete the bottom grid to discover the name of a famous and life-long train enthusiast who used to visit railway stations on an almost daily basis. His work was also often influenced by his love of trains. Who is he?

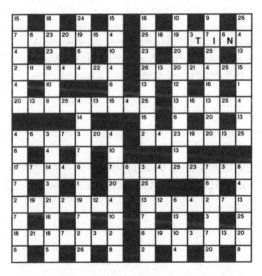

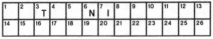

WHAT THEY SAID

The following quotations have some words missing. What are they?

1. **What was Bishop Eric Treacy referring to when he wrote, "What an interesting study of ... a railway station affords"?**
   a) human nature
   b) farewells
   c) architectural style

2. **In his book *American Locomotives: An Engineering History, 1830–1880*, what did Professor John H. White Jr have in mind when he wrote the following: "One of the most neglected topics of locomotive history ..."?**
   a) is the tender
   b) is the boiler
   c) are the wheels

3. **What did American philosopher Ralph Waldo Emerson declare? "Railroads make the country ..."**
   a) accessible
   b) transparent
   c) transform

ON TRACK

Find the start, then, moving one letter at a time – either horizontally, vertically or diagonally – discover something railway companies frequently have to deal with. The answer is made up of two words.

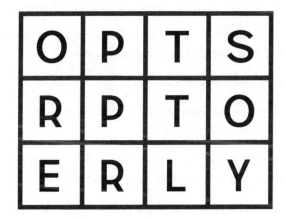

O	P	T	S
R	P	T	O
E	R	L	Y

TRIVIA

1. The Tolstoy Night Train runs between which two capitals?

2. Which American President was nicknamed "The Railsplitter"?

3. Who or what was Skimbleshanks?

4. What train did Crosby, Stills and Nash sing about?

5. The BBC Radio 4 quiz *I'm Sorry I Haven't a Clue* has a game named after which Underground station?

6. What is The Shinkansen?

7. On London Underground maps, what colour is the Hammersmith & City line?

8. Agatha Christie set one of her murder mysteries on a train leaving Paddington at what time?

9. The Volk's Electric Railway is the world's oldest operating electric railway. Where is it?

10. LRC diesel-powered passenger trains operated in some Canadian provinces. The letters LRC each stood for a different feature or aspect of these trains – what were they?

WORD LADDER

The main line (or mainline) has quite a few meanings in railway terminology, but is generally used to describe the principal rail links between major cities and towns, as opposed to branch and suburban lines. In this word ladder, change one letter at a time to turn "main" into "line".

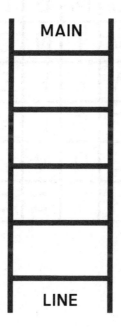

MAIN

LINE

CROSS OUT

Cross out all the letters that appear more than once. The letters that are left, reading from left to right and top to bottom, will spell out a particular type of railway. What is it?

I	G	O	M	B	L	S	P
U	X	V	T	N	Q	W	J
H	D	W	Z	F	E	Y	U
F	J	G	S	L	M	D	X
P	O	E	R	V	Z	T	I
B	A	H	Y	C	Q	N	K

MINI SUDOKU: DELTIC

Deltics were diesel-electric locomotives that entered service in the UK in 1961 and were used for express passenger services on the East Coast Main Line. Twenty-two were built and remained in service until the early 1980s. In this mini sudoku, complete the grid so that every row, column and 2 × 3 box contains the letters that make up "deltic".

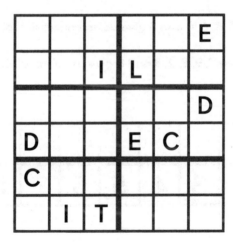

WORD BUILDER

The letters of something important to the railway have been numbered one to nine. Solve the clues to discover what it is.

Letters 1, 5, 2 and 9 give us a fruit

Letters 3, 6, 2 and 7 give us an unforeseen obstacle

Letters 4, 1, 2, 9 and 5 give us something extra

Letters 3, 8, 6, 4 and 5 give us an impression or feeling

Letters 7, 9, 5, 2, 3 and 8 give us some lubricant

1	2	3	4	5	6	7	8	9

A RIDDLE

My first is in train, but not in rail,
My second is in hammer, not in nail.
My third is in fast, not in speed,
My fourth is in crave, never in greed.
My fifth is in kilo, not in ton,
And my whole helps make the trains run.

What am I?

CROSSWORD

Solve the clues and in the shaded squares you will find the name of a famous express train.

Across

7 Elevated railway (8)
9 Pressed (6)
10 Elevator (4)
11 London terminus (10)
12 Blanket-like cloak (6)
14 Comic verse (8)
15 Swallowed (6)
16 Locomotive (6)
19 Quick witty retort (8)
21 Small swelling (6)
23 Voters (10)
24 Gala (4)
25 Assess (4,2)
26 Glistening (8)

Down

1 Game piece (6)
2 Train operating to a port; *The Night Ferry* was one (4)
3 Happy one (anagram) (8)
4 Short railway track (6)
5 At a loss for words (6-4)
6 Paraffin oil (8)
8 Snobbishly pretentious (2-2-2)
13 Device on the front of old American trains to deal with obstacles (10)
15 Secretly and carefully planned (4-4)
17 Absurd ideas (8)
18 Go off the tracks (6)
20 Soldiers (6)
22 Chemical indicator (6)
24 Ticket price (4)

LETTER DROP

The letters in each of the columns need to be entered into the squares immediately below, but not necessarily in the same order. By placing the letters in the correct squares, you will reveal an interesting thought from the Brazilian writer Paulo Coelho.

	E		M		G		S		
	O	A	W	H	O	I	L	A	T	H
T	O	M	K	G	Y	T	T	P	O	T	C	E	I
T	H	R	I	N	R	E	N	T	M	E	R	A	E	N

WORD LINK

Each of the three words in the clues below have a word in common. For example, if the clues were "level", "seller" and "Sunday", the answer would be "best" ("level best", "best seller" and "Sunday best"). Answer each of the following clues correctly to reveal a word in the shaded column, which is something that plays an important part in the running – and sometimes stopping – of the railways. What is it?

1. shower, talk, cry
2. sky, moon, cheese
3. home, over, turn
4. toy, music, spot
5. gift, time, space
6. force, bench, wonders

1			
2			
3			
4			
5			
6			

MYSTERY SUDOKU

Complete the grid so that every row, column and 3 × 3 box contains the letters ADELOPRST in any order. One row or column contains a nine-letter word or name. What is it and why has it become well known?

R	D						E	
		A	P				T	L
					L			A
				P			D	
L			A		S			T
	P			O				
E			T					
P	L				O	R		
	R						S	D

TAKE YOUR PICK

Which of the following is the correct answer? Take your pick.

1. Where would you find Hell railway station?

a) Latvia
b) Estonia
c) Norway

2. What used to be particularly distinctive about railway stations in the Czech Republic?

a) Stations at one time had their own unique jingles.
b) Each station had a major sign painted by a local artist depicting a nearby feature, often a scenic view, building or landmark.
c) Each station had a flagpole flying its own flag.

3. Azuma or British Rail Class 800 Intercity Express Trains are built by Hitachi, but what does Azuma mean in Japanese?

a) Rising sun
b) Swift
c) East

4. In 1808, Richard Trevithick developed a locomotive that was able to pull passengers around a circular cast-iron track he had built in London. It was the first passenger train to charge a fare. What was it called?

a) The Steam Wagon
b) Trev (Short for Trevithick)
c) Catch Me Who Can

FITTING WORDS

Enter the words below horizontally in the grid. When the grid is completed, a word in the shaded boxes will be formed that is something essential to the running of the railways. What is it?

BOGIE

DIESEL

LIVERY

SHUNT

SIDING

STEAM

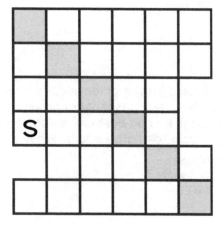

CRYPTOGRAM

Solve the cryptogram to discover what American writer Rogers E. M. Whitaker (also known as E. M. Frimbo) thought about train travel. To give you a start, A = P and G = M.

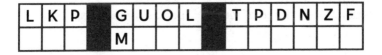

L	K	P		G	U	O	L		T	P	D	N	Z	F
				M										

A	P	N	H	P	M	L		Y	D	F		U	H
P													

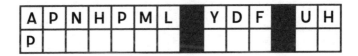

G	U	E	X	T	C		H	N	U	G		U	T	P
M										M				

A	Z	D	M	P		L	U		D	T	U	L	K	P	N
P															

CRISS-CROSS: FISHKIND WAGONS

Many departmental wagons on British Rail were given the names of fish (or aquatic mammals) to help identify their use. So, for instance, a "whiting" was a 14t rail wagon and "winkle" a 22t plate wagon. In this criss-cross, fit all the following wagons into the grid finding a "plaice" for them all.

3-letter names
Cod
Eel

4-letter names
Bass
Carp
Clam
Dace
Hake
Pike

5-letter names
Bream
Brill
Perch

Prawn
Skate
Tench
Trout
Whale

6-letter names
Marlin
Mullet
Mussel
Oyster
Plaice
Salmon
Shrimp
Turbot
Winkle

7-letter names
Halibut
Octopus
Pollock

8-letter names
Goldfish
Mackerel
Pilchard
Starfish
Sturgeon

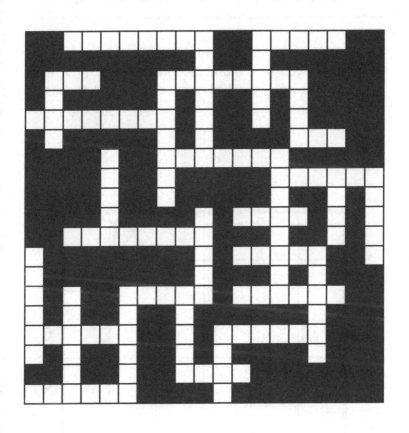

TRAIN TRACKS

Time to lay some tracks to link station A to station B. The numbers tell you how many sections of track go in each column and row. Only straight or curved rails can be used and the track cannot cross itself. Some pieces of the track have already been laid – now it is over to you.

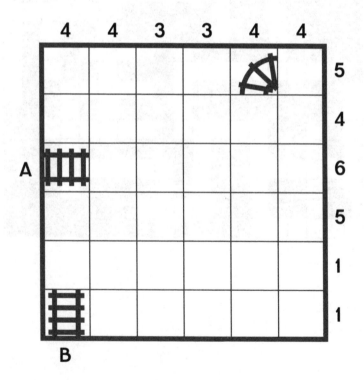

A PERPLEXING POSER

What is that which goes with a steam train, comes with a steam train, is of no use to a steam train and yet the steam train cannot go without it?

STAR OF THE TRACK

The letters of the name of a well-known rail service have been spread evenly around the circle. Find the first letter in the name and follow the letters in order thereby making up the star – and this star of the track. What is the service?

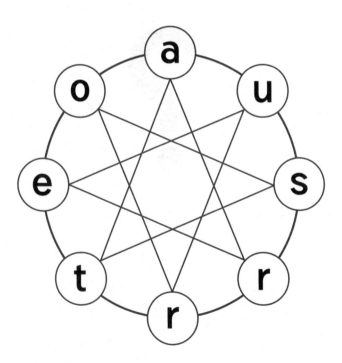

STRANGE BUT TRUE

What was unusual about an early ticket office used at Moreton on Lugg in Herefordshire?

1. It was a shed on an allotment. In addition to tickets, travellers were able to buy freshly picked produce.

2. It was in a hollow oak tree.

3. It was in a converted shepherd's hut.

4. It was in a boat that once sailed on the River Lugg. The cabin was made into a ticket office with travellers having to walk up a short gangplank to get to the office.

5. It was in a public house with the publican doubling up as the station master.

MINI SUDOKU: SUBWAY

We all at some time make use of subways – whether using one to get to a station or catching a subway train. In this mini sudoku, there is a chance to appreciate the subway in another way by completing the grid so that every row, column and 2 × 3 box contains the letters that make up the word "subway".

S		U			W
	U			B	
Y				S	
			A		
	S			Y	

LETTER DROP

The letters in each of the columns need to be entered into the squares immediately below, but not necessarily in the same order. By placing the letters in the correct squares you will discover an amusing exchange that happened a long time ago between an arriving passenger and railway porter.

			O				I				
	O		N	S	O	R	T	O	I	S	
N	N	S	I	R	T	R	D	T	I	N	
I	I	V	C	G	I	Y	A	H	N	T	G	S
			'								
											?
	'					,			'		

WORD BUILDER

The letters of something many travellers appreciate have been numbered one to nine. Solve the clues to discover what it is. The answer is two words.

Letters 1, 8 and 6 give us a flying mammal

Letters 7, 2, 9 and 5 give us a remedy

Letters 4, 8, 7 and 6 give us a reality or truth

Letters 3, 5, 8 and 9 give us dread

And letters 6, 2, 1 and 5 give us a pipe and a form of train travel many readers are familiar with

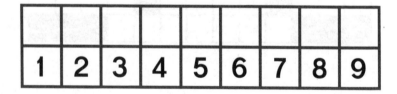

1	**2**	**3**	**4**	**5**	**6**	**7**	**8**	**9**

WORD LADDER

The live rail, or third rail, provides electric power to a locomotive or train through a conductor placed alongside the rails of a railway track. With this essential source of power in mind, charge ahead as you change one letter at a time to turn "live" into "rail".

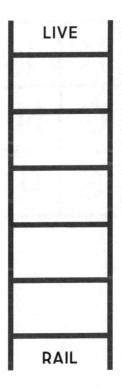

LIVE

RAIL

ON TRACK

Find the start, then moving one letter at a time – either horizontally, vertically or diagonally – discover something important to the functioning of railway companies. What is it?

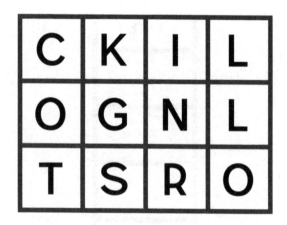

RAILWAY SLANG

There are many slang words used on the railways, but what do the following mean?

1. BOWLING GREEN

a) Tunnel
b) Leaves on line
c) Fast line

2. BANJO

a) Fireman's shovel
b) Baton held by guard
c) Long whistle

3. FISH TAIL

a) A distant signal
b) A swing-arm on a water tower
c) A boat train

4. TRICK

a) Fare dodger
b) A shift or duty
c) Get speed out of an engine

MYSTERY SUDOKU

Complete the grid so that every row, column and 3 × 3 box contains the letters ADEGINROS in any order. One row or column contains a seven-letter station name and something possibly to do at this station.

				G		S		E
		I	S		E		O	
	S	R						
	G	A				O		
N				R				A
	S			N	E			
					D	E		
	G		R		O	I		
R		E		I				

MYSTERY LOCATION

Solve the following clues and in two of the down columns you will discover a certain place. What is this mystery location?

1. Powerful
2. Deduce
3. Small restaurant
4. Draw together
5. Guiding light
6. Alternative

CROSS OUT

Cross out all the letters that appear more than once. The letters that are left, reading from left to right and top to bottom, will spell out an important part of a train. What is it?

C	K	P	W	F	M	T	H
L	J	V	A	X	D	N	S
Y	H	Q	U	Z	R	J	P
S	X	B	T	Y	V	L	F
M	O	D	C	W	K	G	Q
U	A	R	N	I	Z	E	T

WHAT THEY SAID

The following quotations have some of their words missing.
What did the following write or say?

1. What conclusion did the writer G. K. Chesterton come to? "The only way of catching a train I ever discovered is ..."

a) to head to the busiest platform.
b) to allow plenty of time and then some more.
c) to miss the train before.

2. The following was attributed to the engineer Robert Stephenson. What did he believe? "A locomotive engine must be put together ..."

a) with pride, passion and precision.
b) so everything comes together as one.
c) as carefully as a watch.

3. What did broadcaster and journalist Libby Purves consider? "Any railway, working properly, is ..."

a) the most satisfying way to travel.
b) the triumph of painstaking organization.
c) a marvel of civilized co-operation.

CRISS-CROSS: LONDON UNDERGROUND

Many of the following station names will be familiar to travellers of the London Underground, but can you work out how each fits into the grid?

4-letter name
Oval

5-letter name
Angel

6-letter names
Epping
Euston
Kenton
Leyton
Temple

7-letter names
Arsenal
Chesham

Holborn
Kilburn
Mile End
Pimlico

8-letter names
Alperton
Loughton

9-letter names
Colindale
Redbridge
Stratford
Upminster
West Acton
Wimbledon

10-letter names
Camden Town
Dollis Hill
Marylebone
Paddington

11-letter names
Cockfosters
Edgware Road
Northfields

12-letter names
Chancery Lane
Golders Green
London Bridge

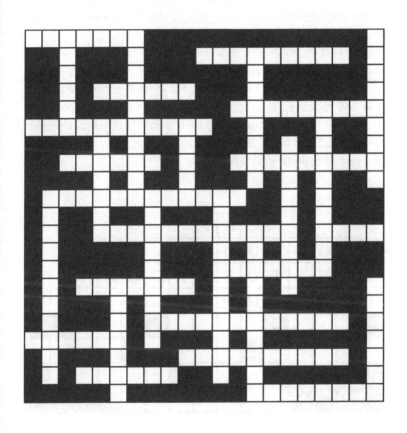

LETTER DROP

The letters in each of the columns need to be entered into the squares immediately below, but not necessarily in the same order. By placing the letters in the correct squares, you will discover a joke that railway enthusiasts may (or may not!) like. The punchline to the joke appears with the solution at the back of this book. What is the joke and can you guess the punchline?

		H	E									
	R	O	O	N	D	O	R	N	R		E	
	H	N	I	T	O	E	I	A	O	O	N	H	A
T	A	A	W	C	H	M	E	S	G	N	T	E	S	T

MAZE

Some journeys can be problematical if trains are rerouted, cancelled or delayed. On one occasion in Texas, due to flooding and the damage caused, it took a train seven years before it could complete its journey. In this maze there are again many obstacles in the way, but can you find a route for the train to take without, hopefully, too long a delay?

TAKE YOUR PICK

Which of the following is the correct answer? Take your pick.

1. Which London Underground station was originally called Great Central?

a) White City

b) Marylebone

c) Bank

2. Which English station has a plaque claiming Paul Simon began writing "Homeward Bound" while sitting on one of its platforms?

a) Widnes

b) Warrington Central

c) Penrith

3. Although Queen Victoria made good use of trains and travelled great distances, what was it she disliked about train travel?

a) The noise

b) The speed

c) The smell and smoke

4. The painter Monet made a dozen oil paintings of which railway terminus in Paris?

a) Gare Saint-Lazare

b) Gare du Nord

c) Gare de l'Est

MYSTERY SUDOKU

Complete the grid so that every row, column and 3 × 3 box contains the letters AEGMORTVY in any order. One row or column contains a seven-letter name of a train. What is it?

		R	Y					O
M	T			E				
O		E	M				R	G
	M			A	G			
			R	M			A	
T	R				V	A		E
			G				M	T
E				R		V		

A PICTURE POSER

What important parts are suggested by the following?

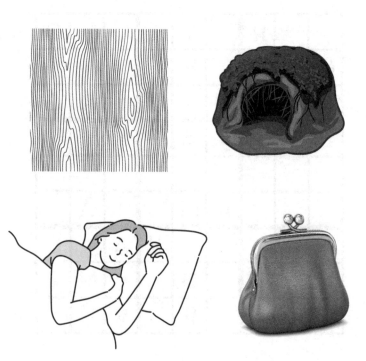

ANAGRAMS

Unscramble the following to reveal some structures, features and buildings connected to the railway.

1. COVERS SELLING

2. NEED HINGES

3. GLIB SAXON

4. AVID CUT

5. GOOD AS DRY

CRYPTOGRAM

Solve the cryptogram to reveal an observation made by the Rev. W. Awdry, creator of *Thomas the Tank Engine*. To give you a start, N = B, J = G, A = F and D = P.

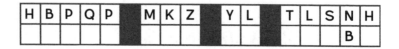

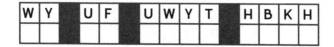

HBPQP MKZ YL TLSNH
WY UF UWYT HBKH
ZHPKU PYJWYPZ KXX
BKT TPAWYWHP
DPQZLYKXWHWPZ

Solution: THERE WAS NO DOUBT IN MY MIND THAT STEAM ENGINES ALL HAD DEFINITE PERSONALITIES

WORD LADDER

Well tank engines are steam locomotives that have water stored in a well on the underside of the locomotive, rather than in a tender. In this word ladder, change one letter at a time to turn "well" into "tank".

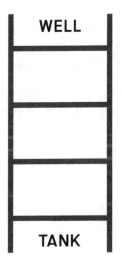

WELL

TANK

STRANGE BUT TRUE

An enterprising person living close to a railway line in the Fens, East Anglia, set up a target in their garden. The crews of passing trains often tried their luck by throwing coal at the target. It was a clever ruse – the crews had fun and the owner of the garden collected up the coal so they never had to buy any fuel. What was the target the gardener set up?

1. A wishing bell. This bell was originally from a ship that foundered off the East Anglian coast. Each time the bell was hit, the person throwing the coal could make a wish.

2. Numbered buckets, so crew members would aim to get the coal they threw into a high-numbered bucket. It became quite competitive with crew members keeping tally of their scores.

3. A big tin cat.

4. A scarecrow mounted on a spring. If hit, it wobbled in comical fashion.

(S)TEAM FOLLOWER

The London & North Eastern Railway (LNER) named some of its Class B17 Gresley 4-6-0 locomotives after famous football clubs. Not only did these locomotives provide many years of service, but they also made popular subjects for model railway enthusiasts. Starting with the circled letter and moving one letter at a time, either horizontally or vertically, find the names of five of these football-named locomotives. All are well-known teams – but which are they?

(L)	I	L	A	E	N	A
E	V	O	R	S	E	L
R	P	O	I	E	V	E
T	S	E	C	L	N	R
E	Y	W	E	S	O	T
R	T	E	D	T	H	A
C	I	T	I	N	U	M

TRAIN TRACKS

Time to lay some tracks to link station A to station B. The numbers tell you how many sections of track go in each column and row. Only straight or curved rails can be used and the track cannot cross itself. Some pieces of the track have already been laid – now it is over to you.

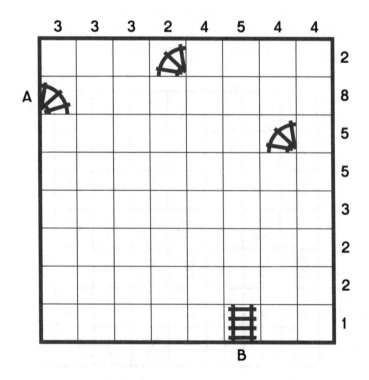

CODED CROSSWORD

In the grid below, each letter of the alphabet has been replaced by a number. To solve the puzzle, you must decide which letter is represented by which number. To help you start, one of the words has been partly filled in. When you have solved the code, complete the bottom grid to discover something that the London & North Eastern Railway lost property office once had to deal with.

A RIDDLE

My first is in signal, but not in stop,
My second is in station, but never found in a shop.
My third is in fuel, but not in water,
While my fourth is in guard, never in porter.
My fifth is in shine, not in light,
And my whole is for railway companies to get right
... and for you also to consider.

What am I?

WORD QUEST: TRAIN

This puzzle gives you a chance to consider the train in another way. Make as many words of three or more letters out of "train" as you can. No proper names allowed.

TRAIN
TAN RAN TARN
TIN RAIN
TAR ART
ANT AIR

TRAIN

12 words = excellent
10 words = very good
8 words = good

CODE BREAKER

Before telephones became widespread, stations and railway offices used electric telegraphs to send messages. To help speed up these messages, a series of codes was devised, each having a precise meaning. The following were used by the Great Western Railway, but can you match the code to its correct meaning?

1. ASPEC   a) Traffic loaded and waiting

2. AFLOW   b) Wire distance and type of road

3. FLASH   c) Time guard came on duty

4. MATIN   d) Arrange treat as special

5. DISTRO   e) Send breakdown van first thing tomorrow morning.

6. BALLOON   f) Give good advance notice of despatch to ...

WORD BUILDER

The letters of something that is often distinctive on locomotives have been numbered one to nine. Solve the clues to discover what it is.

Letters 3, 7 and 5 give us a chart

Letters 8, 2, 6 and 9 give us a story

Letters 1, 4, 7 and 8 give us something tidy

Letters 5, 2, 1, 4 and 6 give us a discussion group

Letters 6, 2, 3, 4, 1 and 8 give us an expression of regret

1	2	3	4	5	6	7	8	9

3 7 5   MAP

MINI SUDOKU: BOILER

Complete the grid so that every row, column and 2 × 3 box contains the letters that make up the word "boiler", the vital chamber in which steam is produced to drive a steam locomotive. Hopefully the complexities of this mini sudoku will not get you too heated.

		I		R	
O					
	B	R			
			B		
				E	L
L				B	

56

STAR OF THE TRACK

The letters of the name of a famous locomotive have been spread evenly around the circle. Find the first letter in the name and follow the letters in order, thereby making up the star – and this star of the track. What is the locomotive? The answer is two words.

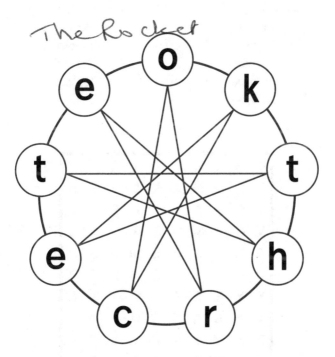

The Rocket

WORD SEARCH: PARIS METRO

Find all the following Parisian Metro stations in the word search and in the remaining squares you will discover another station. What is it?

Anvers	Javel
Balard	Les Halles
Blanche	Nation
Cadet	Opera
Chatelet	Passy
Concorde	Temple
Crimée	Victor Hugo
Gambetta	

O	G	U	H	R	O	T	C	I	V
L	E	S	H	A	L	L	E	S	B
E	C	H	A	T	E	L	E	T	T
V	G	A	M	B	E	T	T	A	E
A	N	V	E	R	S	M	A	B	D
J	N	A	T	I	O	N	P	A	A
S	Y	S	S	A	P	P	T	L	C
I	B	L	A	N	C	H	E	A	E
E	E	M	I	R	C	L	L	R	E
C	O	N	C	O	R	D	E	D	A

LETTER DROP

The letters in each of the columns need to be entered into the squares immediately below, but not necessarily in the same order. By placing the letters in the correct squares you will discover an interesting thought from A. C. Kalmbach writing in *Trains Magazine* in 1954.

			V	N								
	A		S	I	T	I	G	E	E	O	T		R	Q
	H	T		A	C	I	N	L	I	G	N	G		A	E
	H	F	E	A	D	H	U	L	L	V	V	H	R	E	H	R	D	A
W	T	A	L	N	W	S	L	A	O	N	I	E	F	T	E	O	U	S	L

TAKE YOUR PICK

Which is the correct answer? Take your pick.

1. In the original game of *Monopoly*, there were four stations. King's Cross, Liverpool Street and Marylebone were three of them, but what was the fourth?
   a) London Bridge
   b) St Pancras
   c) Fenchurch Street

2. The first locomotive that ran on American soil was the *Stourbridge* ...
   a) *Horse*
   b) *Lion*
   c) *Tiger*

3. Writers have often enjoyed moments of inspiration while travelling on a train. One of the most famous instances was J. K. Rowling having the idea for Harry Potter while on a train journey. Which journey was she taking when the idea occurred?
   a) Edinburgh to London
   b) Manchester to London
   c) Birmingham to London

4. The French state-owned railway SNCF operates Ligne de Cerdagne, which is a scenic route through the Têt Valley into the French Pyrenees. The electric trains operating the route are known by their colour. What is it?
   a) Orange
   b) Yellow
   c) Turquoise

WORD LADDER

The peak hour sees the greatest amount of activity on the railway. In contrast to such a frenetic time, in this word ladder you can take things at a more leisurely pace and, changing one letter at a time, turn "peak" into "hour".

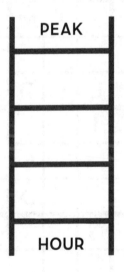

PEAK

HOUR

MYSTERY SUDOKU

Complete the grid so that every row, column and 3 × 3 box contains the letters DEFGHIMRT in any order. One row or column contains a seven-letter word and something of great importance to the railways. What is it?

				T	M		I	
	G	T					E	
I			E		G		D	
			I				M	
G			M		E			R
	I				D			
	E		G		T			H
	F					D	T	
	H		R	D				

WHAT THEY SAID

The following quotes have some of their words missing. What are they?

1. **In his book *The Fascination of Railways*, what had Canon Roger Lloyd got in mind with the statement: "Why is it that however old one gets it is always exciting ..."?**

a) to look out of a railway carriage at the passing scenery.

b) to buy a ticket to somewhere you have never been to before.

c) to have breakfast on a train.

2. **What was the writer Oscar Wilde referring to when he wrote, "I never travel without ..."?**

a) a newspaper.

b) a sick bag.

c) my diary.

3. **John A. Droege wrote much about trains and terminals, but what was he referring to with the following observation: "It has been found by experience that the passengers are likely to become nervous when at windows if ..."?**

a) there is not a large clock in sight.

b) they cannot see the name of the station.

c) it is dirty and they cannot look out.

63

FITTING WORDS

Enter the words below horizontally in the grid. When the grid is completed, an important principle will be highlighted in the shaded boxes. What is it?

ARTWORK
CLOSING
DISTURB
INSULIN
MARCONI
NIAGARA
YOUNGER

					R	
				O		
					N	
		S				

STATION CODES

Computer reservation systems (CRS) codes are a way of identifying places and railway stations are given a three-letter alpha code. As examples, NQY is Newquay, HOT is Henley-on-Thames and LUT is Luton. The following are the codes for which British stations?

1. GLD — GUILDFORD

2. WIM — WIMBLEDON

3. SOU — SOUTHAMPTON

4. NRW — NORWICH

5. LDS — LEEDS

6. BTN — ✗ BOSTON

7. CBG — CAMBRIDGE

8. SHF — SHEFFIELD

9. NHP — NORTHAMPTON

10. BIF — BARROW IN FURNESS

STRANGE BUT TRUE

Some time ago in an Episcopal church in the north of Scotland, a railway porter was helping during the Sunday service by blowing the bellows of the organ. It had been a tiring week and the porter fell asleep. When a church official prodded him, the porter awoke with a start with unexpected consequences. What happened?

1. He reached in his pocket, took out his whistle and blew it with considerable might.

2. He jumped to his feet and roared out, "Change here for Elgin, Lossiemouth and Burghead."

3. He turned to the official who had woken him and said in a booming voice, "Tickets please. Tickets please."

4. He jumped to his feet and with his eyes barely open asked in a loud voice, "Where's the train? I can't see the b****y train."

RAILWAY SLANG

There are many slang words used on the railways, but what do the following mean?

1. NONKER
a) Non-running or cancelled train
b) Locomotive with only a number, no name
c) A navvy

2. ALLELUIA!
a) End of shift
b) A breakdown train with re-railing equipment
c) A signal to shut the tap when washing out a steam locomotive boiler

3. COLLAR WORK
a) Any very heavy task for a steam locomotive
b) To wait in a siding
c) The main administrative office of the railway

4. GREEN PASTURES
a) A cross-country route
b) Freight consisting of cereals
c) High earnings from overtime or bonus payment

HIDDEN NAMES

Hidden in each of the following sentences is the name of a major railway station in England. As an example, in the sentence "The station master looked over the platform," the hidden station is Dover (looke**d over**). What other station names lurk below?

1. The station master says wind on the platform is causing a lot of unpleasantness.

2. Passengers were told to wait over there for departures leaving in the next 15 minutes.

3. People spread in great numbers along the route to see *The Flying Scotsman*.

4. Even though the weather was mediocre, we still caught the train to the seaside.

5. Patsy takes steps to keep her train memorabilia safe.

AT THE JUNCTION

Insert the letters below in the grid. When entered correctly two words are formed, one reading down, the other across. Both of these words share the letter "C" and have a connection with each other. What are they?

ACEEHIIKMNTT

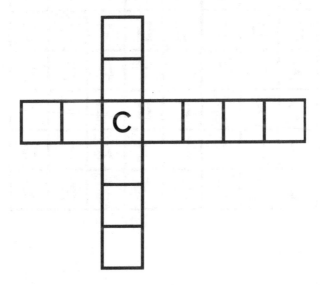

CROSS OUT

Cross out all the letters that appear more than once. The letters that are left, reading from left to right and top to bottom, will spell out a familiar sight on the railways. What is it?

C	H	E	K	M	F	B	Q
L	P	R	J	D	V	S	U
X	U	T	Z	Y	P	C	L
Q	K	W	C	B	M	E	V
J	L	Y	H	X	A	F	D
S	G	K	O	T	Z	N	R

A RIDDLE

My first is in train, but not in steam,
My second is in method, but not in scheme.
My third is in gauge, but not in broad,
My fourth is in alight, but not in board.
My fifth is in speed, not in slow,
And my whole helps decide where to go.

What am I?

WORD LADDER

One of the more familiar signs on the railways is the milepost and other distance markers. One of the original reasons they were installed was that it allowed passengers to verify they had been charged the correct fare for the length of their journey. Now is a chance to reflect on this familiar sight as you change, one letter at a time, "mile" to "post". Given miles are involved, hopefully this will not be too lengthy a process.

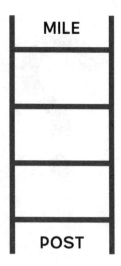

TAKE YOUR PICK

Which of the following is the correct answer? Take your pick.

1. Where was the world's first electric elevated railway?

a) Oslo

b) Liverpool

c) Essen

2. Who, in 1841, did engineer Isambard Kingdom Brunel consider "it was impossible ... to make a good engine-driver"?

a) A man without mechanical skill

b) A man who cannot withstand heat, noise or grime

c) A man who indulged in reading

3. The Seven Stars luxury excursion train was introduced in 2013 to tour a beautiful and mountainous area of which country?

a) Japan

b) New Zealand

c) Canada

4. How did a Parliamentary inquiry sum up the state of Britain's railways in 1917?

a) A riot of individuality

b) Directionless zeal

c) Unregulated chaos

TRAIN TRACKS

Time to lay some tracks to link station A to station B. The numbers tell you how many sections of track go in each column and row. Only straight or curved rails can be used and the track cannot cross itself. Some pieces of the track have already been laid – now it is over to you.

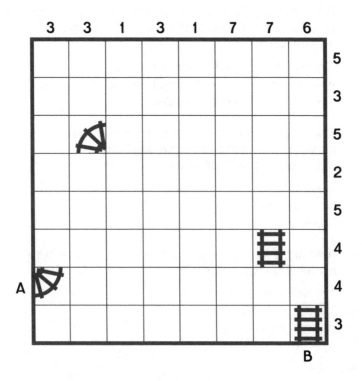

CRYPTOGRAM

Solve the cryptogram to discover an image described by the author that would please many a railway enthusiast. What is it? To give you a start, E = D and V = G.

X	S		J	F	T		Q	F	T	E
										D

N	S		W	A	E		T	S	V	X	S	T
					D				G			

A	W	H	X	S	V	A	Z		U	T	Q	J	W	U	T	E
					G											D

CRISS-CROSS: MODEL RAILWAYS

Planning and building a model railway can bring a great deal of pleasure, with model-railway catalogues offering a great range of stock, scenery as well as many accessories, including some listed below. Find places for all the following in the grid, each of which could embellish many a model railway. Have fun!

3 letters
Inn

4 letters
Cows
Shop

5 letters
House
Sheep

6 letters
Church
Garage
Pylons

7 letters
Lamp hut
Viaduct

8 letters
Fir trees

9 letters
Pillar box
Signal box

10 letters
Buffer stop
Footbridge
Milk churns
Town people
Water tower

11 letters
Granite wall
Waiting room

12 letters
Station hotel

13 letters
Level crossing
Recycling bins
Telegraph pole

14 letters
Railway cottage

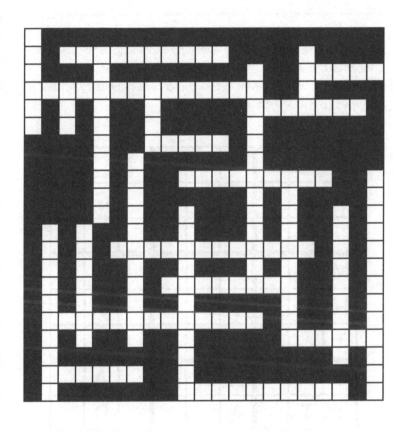

MYSTERY SUDOKU

Complete the grid so that every row, column and 3 × 3 box contains the letters ACDHIMTUV in any order. One row or column contains a seven-letter word and necessity for some railways to run. What is it?

	A				M		C	U
	H			I	T			D
M	C							A
H	D		C		A		T	M
T							V	H
U			H	D			A	
I	T		A				D	

WORD BUILDER

The letters of an important part of a steam train have been numbered one to nine. Solve the clues to discover what it is.

Letters 4, 3 and 5 give us a summit

Letters 6, 9, 7 and 1 give us a bit of foliage

Letters 1, 6, 3 and 5 give us a failure

Letters 8, 2, 4, 7 and 6 give us an aggregate

Letters 4, 9, 7, 5, 3 and 8 give us a brewing vessel

1	2	3	4	5	6	7	8	9

WORD SEARCH: LOCOMOTIVES

Locomotives have often been named after places in the UK. See if you can track down all the following:

Allerton

Ashford

Bedale

Brent

Bury

Buxton

Cricklewood

Dartmoor

Edgeley

Ely

Freshwater

Holyhead

Kidwelly

Leyburn

Loddon

Perth

Plymouth

Runcorn

Swindon

Walsall

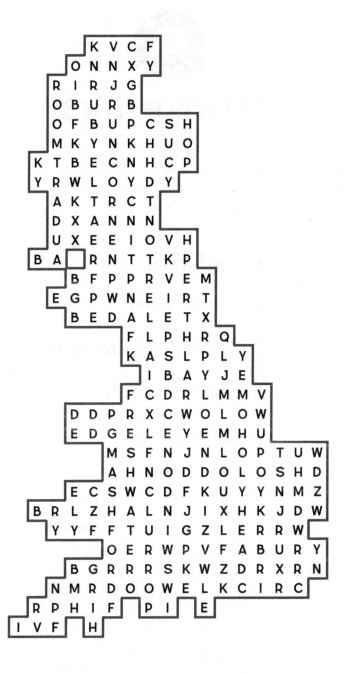

ANAGRAMS

Unscramble the following to reveal personnel you might see at a station or who work on the railways. All play an important and appreciated part. Who are they?

1. CAN REEL

2. CRISP TONE

3. ANOINT MEGASTAR!

4. DART IN RIVER

5. MAIN SLANG

ACROSTICS

Solve the clues correctly and the shaded squares will reveal something that could be of value to rail users. What is it?

1. Move to another track
2. Boredom
3. Loft
4. Utter
5. Oily fruit
6. Darkness

81

CODED CROSSWORD

In the grid below, each letter of the alphabet has been replaced by a number. To solve the puzzle, you must decide which letter is represented by which number. To help you start, one of the words has been partly filled in. When you have solved the code, complete the bottom grid to discover the unlikely saboteurs of a certain Great Western Railway goods train.

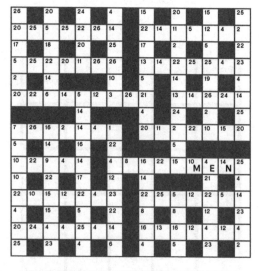

MAZE

When planning a long rail journey there are quite a few options and routes to consider. In this maze, find your way from one station to another. There is only one correct way to go.

LETTER DROP

The letters in each of the columns need to be entered into the squares immediately below, but not necessarily in the same order. By placing the letters in the correct squares you will discover the wording of an eye-catching poster seen in London in 1913.

		N	E	C		R	O			L	N	U			
		F	R	W	E	I	T		H	F	O	D			
	H	E	U	O	D	G	W	G	N	E	A	E	C	N	R
T	P	E	R	B	N	I	T	H	E	R	O	U	V	E	T	D	I	C

TAKE YOUR PICK

Which of the following is the correct answer? Take your pick.

1. In June 2020, an attempt was made by Avanti West Coast to break the UK speed record of 3 hours 52 minutes and 40 seconds between London Euston and Glasgow Central. The attempt on the record, which was set in 1984 by an Advanced Passenger Train, only just failed. By how many seconds did the attempt fail?
a) 11
b) 21
c) 32

2. What is London's least used Underground station?
a) Roding Valley
b) Moor Park
c) Croxley

3. Which country often refers to railways as the "lifeline of the nation"?
a) Brazil
b) Mexico
c) India

4. Deltic D9015/55015 was named "Tulyar". Who or what was Tulyar?
a) Robert Tulyar was an engineer who worked closely with George Stephenson, often called Stephenson's "right-hand man"
b) A racehorse
c) A night-time star

WORD SEARCH: EXPRESSES

Find all the following express trains and in the remaining squares you will discover another famed express. Where applicable, "The" before the express's name has been omitted.

Aberdonian

Comet

Condor

East Anglian

Fair Maid

Grampian

Manxman

Norfolkman

Norseman

Palatine

Royal Scot

Shamrock

Talisman

Waverley

E	N	A	M	K	L	O	F	R	O	N
A	F	A	I	R	M	A	I	D	W	B
S	R	I	E	N	I	T	A	L	A	P
T	A	L	I	S	M	A	N	G	V	T
A	G	R	A	M	P	I	A	N	E	H
N	N	A	M	X	N	A	M	M	R	T
G	N	A	M	E	S	R	O	N	L	O
L	R	O	D	N	O	C	N	B	E	E
I	K	C	O	R	M	A	H	S	Y	L
A	B	E	R	D	O	N	I	A	N	L
N	E	T	O	C	S	L	A	Y	O	R

MINI SUDOKU: POSTER

Posters brighten up many a station as well as advertising attractions, products and forthcoming events. In some past instances, the artwork created for railway posters was considered good enough for prints to be made and books detailing their history were produced. In this mini sudoku, complete the grid so that every row, column and 2 × 3 box contains the letters that make up the word "poster".

	S				T
R	T				
	R		S		
			O	E	
				P	S

FITTING WORDS

Enter the words below horizontally in the grid. When the grid is completed, a word in the shaded boxes will be formed that is something seen on some trains. What is it?

BRAKES

BRIDGE

DEPOT

DRIVER

TRACK

VAN

BETWEEN
THE LINES

Something that is much used on the railways can be inserted in the blank line so that, reading downwards, seven three-letter words are formed. What lies between and certainly under the lines?

E	B	F	O	R	A	S
B	D	Y	D	M	P	Y

WHAT THEY SAID

The following quotes have some of their words missing. What are they?

1. **British engineer and "Father of the Railways" George Stephenson considered, "The rage for railroads is so great that many ..."**

a) parts of the country will now become accessible.
b) towns and industries will greatly expand.
c) will be laid in parts where they will not pay.

2. **Renowned conductor and impresario Sir Thomas Beecham was of the opinion that "Elgar's first symphony is the musical equivalent of ..."**

a) St Pancras Railway Station.
b) Charing Cross Railway Station.
c) King's Cross Railway Station.

3. **In referring to Scranton station in Pennsylvania, Rogers E. M. Whitaker (E. M. Frimbo) wrote, "This station was built for human beings, ..."**

a) with amenities the modern traveller needs.
b) to make them feel welcome and exalted.
c) with style and elegance the main consideration.

ON TRACK

Find the start, then moving one letter at a time – either horizontally, vertically or diagonally – discover something to avoid. The answer is two words. What is it?

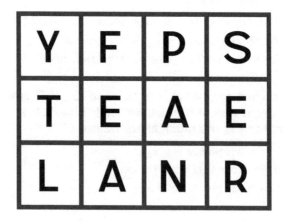

Y	F	P	S
T	E	A	E
L	A	N	R

TRIVIA

1. The *Pines Express* was a holiday express introduced in 1927. It started from Manchester London Road and ran to which south coast resort?

2. Which is the deepest station on the London Underground?

3. According to the song made famous by Gladys Knight and the Pips, where did the Midnight Train go?

4. The "Empire Builder" is Amtrak's busiest long-distance train and goes to Seattle and Portland? In which major American city does the 2,206-mile route start?

5. What is the BedPan line?

6. He became well known for his railway guides and timetables and lived from 1800 to 1853. Who was he?

7. The main entrance to which station is known as the Victory Arch and is a Grade II listed building?

8. What is the Pandrol Clip used for?

9. What does the railway abbreviation OHL mean?

10. What fully automated railway opened in London in 1987?

CRYPTOGRAM

Solve the cryptogram to discover some thoughts of English humorist and politician A. P. Herbert. To give you a start, F = L and I = P.

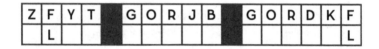

SLOW TRAIN TRAVEL

IS ALMOST THE ONLY

RESTFUL EXPERIENCE

THAT IS LEFT TO US.

I LOVE IT

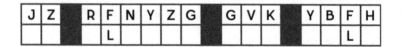

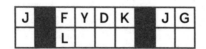

WORD SEARCH: LOST RAILWAY

Sadly, many railways have been lost and closed, but somewhere in the grid below a railway still survives. Among all the letters can you find the one remaining railway?

R	I	A	W	R	A	I	Y	W	A	R	I	A	R	Y
W	R	I	Y	L	R	Y	I	W	R	A	I	R	A	R
A	A	L	R	A	W	R	R	L	R	I	R	A	R	I
R	L	A	Y	R	Y	I	A	R	A	L	Y	R	Y	L
A	I	R	W	I	W	R	W	Y	L	W	R	L	A	R
R	A	I	A	R	A	L	Y	R	A	Y	L	A	R	W
I	L	W	R	L	Y	I	Y	I	R	A	W	I	A	R
A	R	I	Y	A	R	W	A	R	Y	L	R	A	I	Y
W	A	R	R	L	A	I	R	A	I	R	Y	R	A	R
L	R	I	W	R	I	W	A	Y	I	W	A	Y	W	A
R	L	I	A	R	L	W	L	R	A	I	L	A	R	W
R	A	Y	A	W	Y	I	A	R	L	A	W	L	A	R
Y	R	A	L	A	R	R	Y	W	I	L	A	Y	R	A
A	I	W	R	I	A	Y	A	Y	I	R	Y	I	W	R
R	A	I	A	L	W	Y	L	I	R	A	I	Y	R	I

WORD LADDER

American author Ray Bradbury was a great fan of the subway and once said, "Sometimes I ride the subway all day." This way he could watch people and "figure out who they are and what they want and where they're going". Now is a chance to figure out the subway in another way and, changing one letter at a time, turn "sub" into "way".

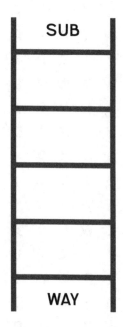

SUB

WAY

ANAGRAMS

Unscramble the following to reveal the names of London stations.

1. SCRAP ANTS

2. THE CURRENT CHEFS

3. NO GOLDEN BIRD

4. LOVELIEST REPORT

5. NOT USE

WORD BUILDER

The letters of a certain type of train have been numbered one to nine. Solve the clues to discover what it is.

Letters 5, 8 and 2 give us a number to start with

Letters 9, 7 and 6 give us a lubricant

Letters 1, 5, 3 and 4 give us a small lake

Letters 1, 7, 6 and 2 give us a heap

And appropriately letters 2, 8 and 4 give us the finale

1	2	3	4	5	6	7	8	9

HIDDEN NAMES

Some diesel-electric locomotives were given male names and hidden in each of the following sentences is one of these. As an example, in the sentence, "If redirected, all the passengers should make up the time they lost while waiting," the hidden name is Fred (I**f red**irected). What other names can you find below?

1. The holidaymaker was not sure whether to struggle with his luggage or get a trolley.

2. The station has plans to install a super cybercafe before the end of the year.

3. Tenders have gone out for a new type terminal which will handle greater passenger numbers.

4. The driver thought the new route was better. "I can also see passengers preferring it," he added.

5. The new lilac livery has proved popular with rail users.

RAILWAY SLANG

There are many slang words used on the railways, but what do the following mean?

1. CAULIFLOWER
a) The yellowy green livery favoured by some companies
b) Locomotive with crested front
c) Trains carrying farm produce

2. UNDER THE ARM
a) Signal gantry
b) Level crossing
c) Not up to standard

3. RINGER
a) Crowbar
b) Whistle board or post
c) Engine cleaner

4. FLYING DUCK
a) Section insulator
b) Oscillating guard's van
c) Travelling ticket inspector

MYSTERY SUDOKU

Complete the grid so that every row, column and 3 × 3 box contains the letters EFHIMNORU in any order. One row or column contains a seven-letter word, which is something that is important to the role of railway staff. What is it?

		F	H			O	N	
U				R				
O	H	M			E			
	E							M
H			N		M			F
F							O	
			M			N	E	H
			R					O
	I	E			N	R		

CRISS-CROSS: AMTRAK ROUTES

Amtrak runs more than 30 train routes throughout the United States and several in Canada. Some of these routes and services are listed below. Find places for them all in the map.

5 letters
Acela

8 letters
Cardinal
Crescent
Palmetto
Piedmont

9 letters
Maple Leaf
Vermonter

10 letters
Adirondack
Downeaster
Texas Eagle

11 letters
San Joaquins
Valley Flyer

13 letters
Pennsylvanian
Sunset Limited

14 letters
Capitol Limited
Heartland Flyer
Southwest Chief

15 letters
Capitol Corridor

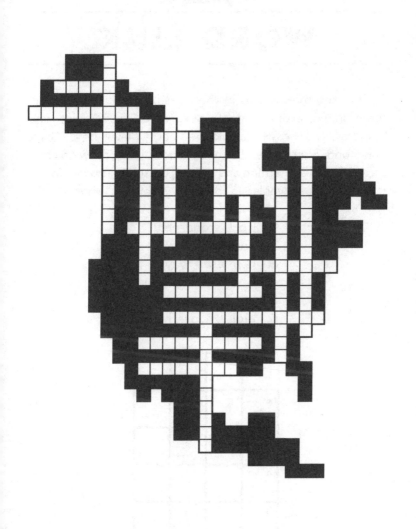

WORD LINK

Each of the three words in the clues below have a word in common. For example, if the clues were "level", "seller" and "Sunday", the answer would be "best" ("level best", "best seller" and "Sunday best"). Answer each of the following clues correctly and something that serves a useful purpose on the railways will be revealed in the shaded column. What is it?

1. track, stand, hold
2. back, road, away
3. home, self, way
4. line, course, reason
5. hands, more, too
6. praise, hopes, horse

1			
2			
3			
4			
5			
6			

LETTER DROP

The letters in each of the columns need to be entered into the squares immediately below, but not necessarily in the same order. By placing the letters in the correct squares you will discover an observation from the writer A. A. Milne that is one many readers are likely to share.

	I	N			N				A	R		I	
H	A	W	K	E	S	E		H	T	N	P	I	L
T	N	O	S	H	I	R	O	A	C	A	P	A	I	N	Y

TRAIN TRACKS

Time to lay some tracks to link station A to station B. The numbers tell you how many sections of track go in each column and row. Only straight or curved rails can be used and the track cannot cross itself. Some pieces of the track have already been laid – now it is over to you.

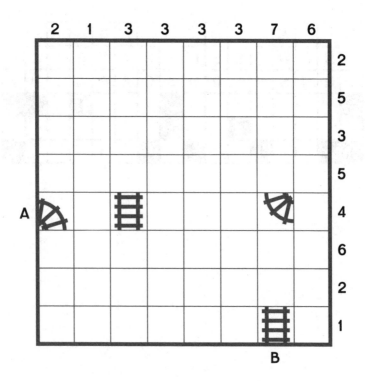

STAR OF
THE TRACK

The letters of the name of a famous locomotive have been spread evenly around the circle. Find the first letter in the name and follow the letters in order thereby making up the star – and this historic star of the track. What is it?

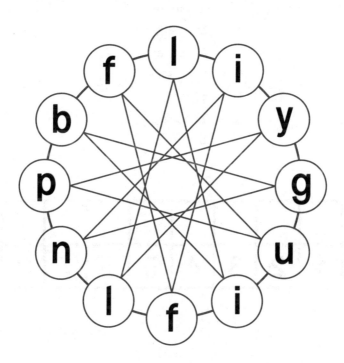

MIND THE GAP

Each of the following words is missing a letter. Put the missing letter into the grid below to reveal something used – as well as wanted – by passengers. What is it?

1. _atch   p e w h
2. sp_re   a i o
3. _elay   d r
4. cu_ed   r b
5. _tems   i s
6. sh_re   a i o
7. _oing   t g
8. ad_pt   e o a o

C	A	R	R	I	A	G	E
1	2	3	4	5	6	7	8

STRANGE BUT TRUE

Early in this millennium, what happened to New York City Municipal Transportation Authority's old subway cars?

1. They were sold to holiday camps for conversion into holiday homes.

2. They were disposed of at sea.

3. They were turned into cafe cars. Many were sold to heritage railways where visitors could sit in them enjoying some refreshment.

4. They were sold to a Canadian theme park where they transported visitors around the grounds.

5. They were sold to fire departments for use in fire training as well as by other emergency departments.

MINI SUDOKU: SIGNAL

Signals can indicate a great many things to drivers, including giving authority to proceed and the state of the line ahead. In this mini sudoku, the way is clear to go ahead and complete the grid so that every row, column and 2 × 3 box contains the letters that make up the word "signal".

		N		S	
I				A	N
	N		A		G
A		L			

ACROSTICS

Solve the clues correctly and the shaded squares will reveal something of interest.

1. Begin
2. Teacher
3. Additional
4. Legal defence
5. Large fruit

1				
2				
3				
4				
5				

A PERPLEXING POSER

BET I'M LATE

Rearrange the letters to find a possible solution.

WORD QUEST: RAILWAY

Make as many words of three or more letters out of "railway" as you can. No proper names allowed.

RAILWAY

27 words = excellent
22 words = very good
20 words = good

ON TRACK

Find the start, then moving one letter at a time – either horizontally, vertically or diagonally – discover something many passengers appreciate. What is it?

M	S	W	N
O	A	G	I
O	R	I	T

TAKE YOUR PICK

Which of the following is the correct answer? Take your pick.

1. **London was the first city in the world to have an underground railway. What was the second?**
a) Budapest
b) Paris
c) New York

2. **What was unusual about Dartmouth station, which closed in 1968?**
a) As the station was often used by naval officers travelling to the Britannia Royal Naval College at Dartmouth, it had a separate platform just for use by the naval authorities. On occasion this platform was used for the transfer of prisoners to Dartmoor Prison.
b) Due to subsidence, the station was separated from the platforms by a road, which pedestrians could either access by bridge or pedestrian crossing.
c) It had no trains.

3. **On 28 April 1869, during the construction of the Central Pacific Railroad and with a team of over 4,000 men, railroad executive Charles Crocker managed the laying of a great length of track. How many miles of single track were laid on that one day?**
a) 10 miles 56 feet
b) 12 miles 39 feet
c) 14 miles 29 feet

4. **What was the Withered Arm?**
a) A long narrow siding at Clapham Junction.
b) The routes west of Exeter that served many remote parts of Devon and Cornwall.
c) The railway line that crosses Rannoch Moor in Scotland.

WORD SEARCH: AT THE STATION

On any trip to a station you are likely to see some or all of the following, but can you find them in the grid?

Barrier

Concourse

Departure board

Escalator

Information desk

Kiosks

Platform

Restaurants

Shops

Stairs

Taxi rank

Ticket machine

Ticket office

Timetable

Trains

Trolley

Turnstile

Waiting room

```
S D E P A R T U R E B O A R D D T
L P E G X F E L I T S N R U T M G
S V O H E B N V I M P Q T E K O O
R T I H T C J U R L N J I S L O A
O K N E S F I O G S G R E R R R E
T Z Z A S K F F K L M D T U P G L
A V Q K R T Z S F G N K U O F N B
L J D T A U O N F O O D E C K I A
A L P L P I A C I S T R C N Q T T
C P P N K T T T N O T E D O A I E
S P P Y W R A M S Y G A K C D A M
E W E X O M G X T E K N I C Q W I
B Z R L R O K E I R R O B R I O T
S O L O Q T W T L R Q J V D S T K
Q E F E H Q W S H U A T R A I N S
Y N I Q R E I R R A B N E N E V R
I D Q E N I H C A M T E K C I T Y
```

ANAGRAMS

Unscramble the following to reveal the names of some famous trains and locomotives.

1. NO SELF-ACTING MYTHS

2. SENIOR EXPERTS

3. OUR RATES

4. SERENE TRIP

5. LOG ON REWARD

WHAT THEY SAID

The following quotes have some of their words missing. What are they?

1. **In her book *Murder on the Orient Express*, what did Agatha Christie consider when she wrote "Conversations on the platform, before the departure of a train, are ..."?**

a) rather hurried affairs.
b) often indistinct.
c) apt to be somewhat repetitive in character.

2. **What did the Turkish writer Mehmet Murat ildan write? "The simplicity of a train's success strategy is admirable: ..."**

a) move forward and reach your destination.
b) fast, efficient and reliable.
c) connect the places where people need to go.

3. **The distinguished engineer and innovator Oliver Bulleid said, in talking about Sir Nigel Gresley, "He was incapable of ill-temper, but what I appreciated most was ..."**

a) his determination to create and design the best.
b) his wide-ranging interest in all engineering.
c) his passion for railways.

MYSTERY SUDOKU

Complete the grid so that every row, column and 3 × 3 box contains the letters ADEHILNOS in any order. One row or column contains an eight-letter word and an important factor in the operation of the railways. What is it?

				E		S	L	
		S		D				N
					S	H		
E			L		O			I
		O				A		
H			D		N			O
		N	H					
A				S		O		
	O	E		L				

WORD LADDER

A "headcode" is an arrangement of lights, discs, letters and numbers on the front of a train indicating the type of train and/or its route. In this word ladder, changing one letter at a time, turn "head" into "code". At least with this puzzle you get a "head" start.

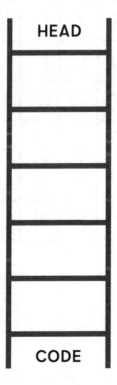

HEAD

CODE

CROSS OUT

Cross out all the letters that appear more than once. The letters that are left, reading from left to right and top to bottom, will spell out something you may hear about on the railways. What is it?

P	T	Y	A	C	Q	G	I
E	B	U	D	F	V	J	M
Z	H	K	W	M	L	X	S
D	A	T	X	P	C	K	J
S	Y	V	B	Z	Q	O	F
L	R	I	E	N	U	G	W

A RIDDLE

My first is in diesel, but not in fuel,
My second is in rivet, not in tool.
My third is in punctual, but is never in late,
My fourth is in foot, but not in plate.
My fifth is in ticket, but is not in free,
And my whole is a busy place to be.

What am I?

ACROSTICS

Solve the clues correctly and the shaded squares will reveal a feature often seen on the railways. What is it?

1. Short railway track
2. Large lizard
3. Cultivated area
4. Lump of gold
5. Fix firmly and stably
6. Indulgence

1					
2					
3					
4					
5					
6					

STRANGE BUT TRUE

During the First World War, Sir Edward Henry, who was commissioner of police at Scotland Yard, was asked by a newly appointed ticket inspector if he had a ticket for his Scottie dog. Sir Edward expressed surprise, as he did not know his dog was there and said it must have followed him. He was also unaware that the dog needed a ticket. What were the consequences?

1. The little Scottie dog was very protective of Sir Edward, and when he saw him being challenged, jumped up and gave the inspector a nip. The incident was widely reported, much to the embarrassment of Sir Edward. After this, London Underground insisted that all dogs had to be on leads when at stations or travelling.

2. The ticket inspector did not believe Sir Edward when he said he did not know his dog was following him. During a heated exchange at the station entrance, a policeman who was patrolling the area came over and started to question Sir Edward, unaware he was the commissioner. The incident was seen by a journalist, with a report and cartoon appearing in a national newspaper the next day.

3. As Sir Edward had said he was unaware of dogs requiring a ticket to travel, to clear up any misunderstanding, London Underground started an advertising campaign with dogs needing a "rover ticket" to travel. To appease Sir Edward, a picture of his Scottie dog was used in some of the posters.

4. Following the incident, and as a goodwill gesture, London Underground sent Sir Edward a season ticket made out to "Sir Edward Henry's dog".

WORD BUILDER

Something many rail users appreciate has been numbered one to nine. The answer is two words, but what is it?

Letters 6, 8 and 3 give us railway slang for a signal arm

Letters 5, 1, 7 and 9 give us a place for maintenance

Letters 9, 2 and 6 give us a decline

Letters 4, 2, 9 and 8 give us animal skin

Letters 9, 2, 5 and 1 give us a bowl

Letters 5, 2, 7, 3 and 8 give us a blockade

1	2	3	4	5	6	7	8	9

WORD LINK

Each of the three words in the clues below have a word in common. For example, if the clues were "level", "seller" and "Sunday", the answer would be "best" ("level best", "best seller" and "Sunday best"). Answer each of the following clues correctly and something always happening on the railways will be revealed in the shaded column. What is it?

1. lots, back, level
2. here, miss, enough
3. mind, plan, space
4. ready, prize, sale
5. box, shop, horse
6. behind, kick, cough
7. car, well, ill

1			
2			
3			
4			
5			
6			
7			

LETTER DROP

The letters in each of the columns need to be entered into the squares immediately below, but not necessarily in the same order. By placing the letters in the correct squares you will discover an observation from the writer E. M. Forster.

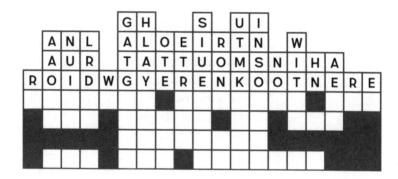

A PERPLEXING POSER

On a late-night train, someone pulled the emergency alarm cord. The guard quickly realized it had been pulled as a prank by one of four individuals, all the worse for wear. The guard asked each one who had pulled the cord and they replied as follows.

Emma said, "Don't look at me. It was Nick who pulled the cord."

Nick shook his head, "No, it was Susie who pulled the cord."

Jim smiled and looked the guard squarely in the eye, "I didn't pull the cord."

The guard looked at the last of the four, "Well?" he asked.

Susie sighed. "If you ask me, Nick is lying."

**Only one of the four replies is the truth.
Who pulled the cord?**

MINI SUDOKU: LIVERY

Railway companies take much pride in their liveries, which help to promote their brand, look and identity. In this mini sudoku you can consider this all-important feature in more detail so that every row, column and 2 × 3 box contains the letters that make up the word "livery".

V			E		
	Y			V	
R		Y		L	
				E	
	I		L	R	

STAR OF
THE TRACK

The letters of the name of a famous train have been spread evenly around the circle. Find the first letter in the name and follow the letters in order thereby making up the star – and this star of the track. What is the train?

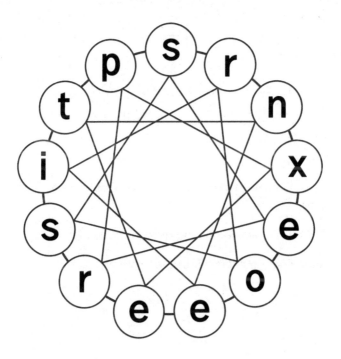

HIDDEN NAMES

Pullman trains and coaches offered style and, as one publication mentioned, were "so comfortable that when once aboard one is able to forget austerity and utility and indulge in a feeling of well-being and luxury". Another endearing feature was that non-driving cars were all given female names. In each of the following sentences a name given to one of these cars is hidden. As an example, in the sentence, "The new carriages had orange upholstery," the hidden name is Dora (ha**d ora**nge). Can you find the five hidden female names?

1. I was really pleased to see Mum on a special heritage train.

2. The train is just departing. We now expect to arrive at midday.

3. By buying her ticket early, she was able to save rather a lot.

4. The repair involved fitting quite a costly dial.

5. Annoyingly she left her bag at Harrow station.

TAKE YOUR PICK

Which of the following is the correct answer? Take your pick.

1. Where was the world's first mountain-climbing cog railway?
a) Schafberg, Austria
b) Snowdon, Wales
c) Mount Washington, New Hampshire, USA

2. According to a paper presented to the Institute of Transport in 1953, in a locomotive's 40 years' life expectancy, how many of those years would be spent in revenue-earning service?
a) 12 years
b) 16 years
c) 21 years

3. The celebrated artist Terence Cuneo painted many railway scenes, but he also included something extra in many of his paintings. What did he include?
a) A bird
b) A dog
c) A mouse

4. British Rail Class 50 diesel locomotives had a nickname because of the noise they originally made. What was it?
a) Bee, because of a humming sound they emitted
b) Hairdryer, because of the whirring sound they made
c) Hoover, as these locomotives made a noise like a vacuum cleaner

ON TRACK

Find the start, then moving one letter at a time – either horizontally, vertically or diagonally – discover something many passengers appreciate. What is it?

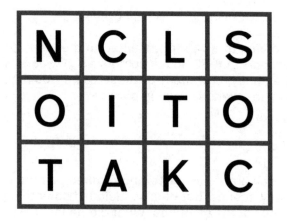

N	C	L	S
O	I	T	O
T	A	K	C

MYSTERY SUDOKU

Complete the grid so that every row, column and 3 × 3 box contains the letters ADIMORSTU in any order. One row or column contains a seven-letter word and beneficiary of the railways. What is it?

		T			M			
	A	S						
	M			T	U			I
O				S			M	
		A				O		
	U			R				S
I			O	A			R	
						M	D	
			M			T		

ANAGRAMS

Unscramble the anagrams to reveal the names of some major UK stations. The first two are Scottish, the third Welsh and last two are in England.

1. BRAVELY WEIGH UNDER

2. WRONG GATE CALLS

3. CLAD FINER CRAFT

4. ADMIT STEEL PROBLEMS

5. ADVERTS EXISTED

RAILWAY SLANG

There are many slang words used on the railways, but what do the following mean?

1. BLINKERS

a) An unlit semaphore signal lamp
b) Smoke deflectors
c) Auxiliary lights on a locomotive

2. ABADAN

a) A spur line
b) A luggage van
c) Driver using much oil

3. RAFT

a) Train carrying liquid freight
b) Two or more wagons coupled together
c) A boat train

4. MUCKBIRD

a) Dirty oil waste
b) Thick black or dark smoke emitting from a steam engine
c) Fireman or stoker

WORD SEARCH: LONDON UNDERGROUND

Time for some underground delving as you seek out the following London Underground stations.

Aldgate	Earls Court	Perivale
Alperton	East Ham	Pimlico
Amersham	Edgware Road	Pinner
Angel	Epping	Richmond
Archway	Euston	Rickmansworth
Arsenal	Holborn	Royal Oak
Balham	Kenton	Ruislip
Barking	Kilburn	Stratford
Blackfriars	Kingsbury	Temple
Bond Street	Leyton	Tower Hill
Burnt Oak	Mile End	Victoria
Chesham	Northfields	West Ham
Cockfosters	Northwood	
Dollis Hill	Oval	

```
E G G M Y N O T R E P L A C J V M I Y
R I C H M O N D Z R O Y A L O A K A A
K I Y R U B S G N I K V I Q H E G S I
A N C N O R T H F I E L D S T N H B R
C O C K F O S T E R S M R A O O L U O
Y C T E M P L E G T A E G R L A P R T
C H E S H A M V R H M D T B C I Y N C
E L D Y R U N A T A L H O K N E N T I
A D A D L N T S N A W R F N U P T O V
E A G V N F A O W O N R E E P E E A D
A N F W O E T R O O I R T P I L E K O
R G K R A N E D C A R N S P L A R Y L
L E D X E R R L R H N T N I S V T A L
S L Z K G E E S I N W O H N I I S R I
C R K I L B U R N M P A T G U R D S S
O C I L M I P S O P P O Y Y R E N E H
U M A H T S E W T A X C V T E P O N I
R B M A H L A B A O D C U V B L B A L
T O W E R H I L L G N I K R A B H L L
```

WORD LADDER

Maintained by the Rail Safety and Standards Board, the rule book contains sets of instructions rail staff must follow. In this word ladder, you too need to follow the rules and, changing one letter at a time, turn "rule" into "book".

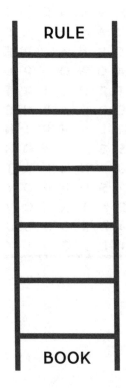

RULE

BOOK

TRAIN TRACKS

Time to lay some tracks to link station A to station B. The numbers tell you how many sections of track go in each column and row. Only straight or curved rails can be used and the track cannot cross itself. Some pieces of the track have already been laid – now it is over to you.

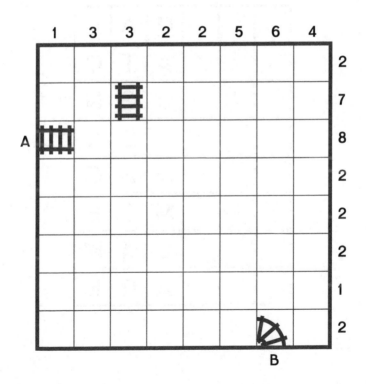

DOWN WORD

Place a three-letter word in the spaces in each row to complete a six-letter word. When the grid is completed correctly, a new word in the shaded letters will be formed and something important to the railways. What is it?

			U	A	L
			A	T	O
			U	G	N
			L	E	R
			M	E	G
			M	I	E
			L	A	M
			A	D	E

RAILWAY LINES

There have been many great books and works based on the railways. Some are listed below. Match the book (or short story) with the author who penned the lines.

1. *Strangers on a Train*

2. *Stamboul Train*

3. *The Mystery of the Blue Train*

4. *The Girl on the Train*

5. *The Railway Children*

6. *Avalanche Express*

7. *Thomas the Tank Engine*

8. "The Signal-Man" (short story)

9. *The Railway Detective* (series)

10. *The Man Who Watched the Trains Go By*

a) Graham Greene

b) E. Nesbit

c) Rev. W. Awdry

d) Georges Simenon

e) Patricia Highsmith

f) Charles Dickens

g) Paula Hawkins

h) Edward Marston

i) Colin Forbes

j) Agatha Christie

X MARKS THE SPOT

Enter the following words correctly and in the shaded squares you will discover a mystery place. To give you a start, some letters have already been entered. X marks what spot?

ADVISORY
BECOMING
CALENDAR
CANISTER
ELEPHANT
LISTENER
OUTDATED
SORCERER

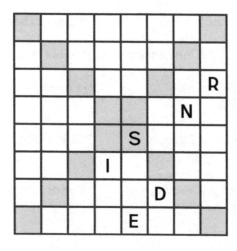

CRYPTOGRAM

Solve the cryptogram to discover an observation from Canon Roger Lloyd and one many readers are likely to share. To give you a start, N = S, Q = D and I = M.

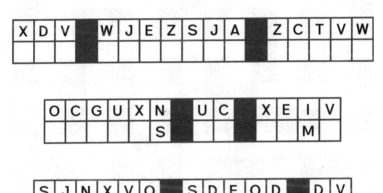

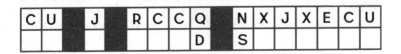

X	D	V		W	J	E	Z	S	J	A		Z	C	T	V	W
T	H	E		R	A	I	L	W	A	Y		L	O	V	E	R

O	C	G	U	X	N		U	C		X	E	I	V
C	O	U	N	T	S		N	O		T	I	M	E

S	J	N	X	V	Q		S	D	E	O	D		D	V
W	A	S	T	E	D		W	H	I	C	H		H	E

N	K	V	U	Q	N		N	J	G	U	X	V	W	E	U	R
S	P	E	N	D	S		S	A	U	N	T	E	R	I	N	G

C	U		J		R	C	C	Q		N	X	J	X	E	C	U
O	N		A		G	O	O	D		S	T	A	T	I	O	N

141

CROSSWORD

Solve the clues and in the shaded squares you will find the name of a famous train. Where does it run?

Across

1 Underground railway (6)
4 Bandage (6)
9 A very short branch line (4)
10 Go backwards (10)
11 Throw off track (6)
12 Value highly (8)
13 Train manager (9)
15 Railway track (4)
16 Bean protein (4)
17 Train cord (9)
21 Delay (8)
22 Security (6)
24 Carving on ship's bow (10)
25 Fried potato (4)
26 XC (6)
27 Air travel fatigue (3,3)

Down

1 Overall chief (7)
2 Myanmar (5)
3 Kind of paint (7)
5 Type of sleeper (6)
6 Mechanical gate seen at some stations (9)
7 Sanction (7)
8 Railway official (7,6)
14 Type of ticket (3,6)
16 Terminus (7)
18 Remainder (7)
19 Sometimes necessary for a rail track to maintain a shallow gradient (7)
20 Another type of 5 down (6)
23 Central (5)

BETWEEN THE LINES

Something that is an important consideration on the railways can be inserted in the blank line so that, reading downwards, eight three-letter words are formed. What lies between the lines?

A	M	A	F	E	R	S	D
K	T	T	N	A	B	Y	E

MINI SUDOKU: POINTS

Points are the movable sections of tracks that allow trains to move from one line to another and determine the route to be taken. The route to be taken now, though, is to complete the grid so that every row, column and 2 × 3 box contains the letters that make up the word "points".

P	O				
		T	N		P
		S			N
				I	
				T	
			P		S

TRIVIA

1. The *Mayflower* passenger train service starts and ends where?

2. What does the abbreviation GUV stand for?

3. What is a ferroequinologist?

4. Which locomotive broke the world speed record for steam locomotives at 126 mph on 3 July 1938?

5. Which London Underground line has the most stations?

6. Where and what was the "Dockers' Umbrella"?

7. Which famous author was involved in the derailment at Staplehurst in July 1865? His son said his father never fully recovered from the trauma.

8. J. K. Rowling used which station and platform as a gateway to a world of comradeship and magic?

9. Ironically, there is no lake at Lake, although it is by the sea, but where in the UK is Lake station?

10. The *Ghan* offers one of the world's greatest rail journeys. Where does it run?

STRANGE
BUT TRUE

In the 1880s James Wide was a signalman for the Cape Town–Port Elizabeth Railway. He was ably assisted by Jack, but who was Jack?

1. His eight-year-old son. Jack had aspirations of becoming a signalman and the railway authorities allowed him to work with his father under strict supervision. As soon as Jack left school he joined the railway, proudly taking over the signal box when his father retired. Jack later became head engineer of the railway.

2. A baboon. Due to an injury, James Wide trained this baboon to assist him with certain duties in the signal box.

3. A cocker spaniel owned by a local station master. As the station master did not want Jack to be alone all day, James was given permission to look after Jack in the signal box. Jack barked at the approach of each train making sure James was always kept fully aware. When Jack "retired", the station authorities gave him a medal for his collar and an inscribed dog bowl thanking him for his services.

4. A carrier pigeon. James raced carrier pigeons and at times used Jack to fly to carry messages to the nearby station.

WORD SEARCH

At one time, the rail network covered much of the Isle of Wight and, during its heyday, some train crews made the most of rural lines by throwing coal at game they saw and bagging pheasants. The authorities decided to act and issued a notice: "The practice of throwing fuel at game... must cease forthwith." To discover the consequence, find all the following locomotives named after Isle of Wight towns and villages in the grid opposite and the remaining letters will tell you the outcome.

Ashey

Alverstone

Bembridge

Bonchurch

Brading

Chale

Cowes

Fishbourne

Godshill

Merstone

Newport

Sandown

Seaview

Totland

Ventnor

N	U	E	E	L	A	H	C	S	E	A
W	D	G	O	D	S	H	I	L	L	L
O	S	D	T	Y	E	H	S	A	O	V
D	F	I	S	H	B	O	U	R	N	E
N	V	R	W	E	I	V	A	E	S	R
A	E	B	D	N	A	L	T	O	T	S
S	N	M	E	R	S	T	O	N	E	T
N	T	E	E	S	S	E	W	O	C	O
I	N	B	R	A	D	I	N	G	N	N
B	O	N	C	H	U	R	C	H	S	E
T	R	O	P	W	E	N	T	E	A	D

ON THE
RIGHT TRACK

Starting with the circled letter and moving one letter at a time, either horizontally, vertically or diagonally, discover something of potential importance. The answer is two words.

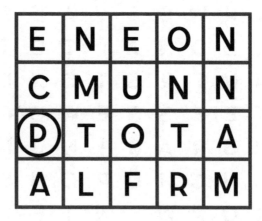

E	N	E	O	N
C	M	U	N	N
(P)	T	O	T	A
A	L	F	R	M

TAKE YOUR PICK

Which of the following is the correct answer? Take your pick.

1. **In the Rainhill Trials, held in 1829 to assess the reliability of steam locomotives of the time, why was Thomas Shaw Brandreth's *Cycloped* considered unsuitable?**

a) It was not a steam locomotive but used a horse on a treadmill to turn the wheels.

b) It was considered unsafe and "posed serious danger" to those who tried to operate (or even went near) the flimsy engine.

c) Despite generating huge amounts of steam, the locomotive refused to move and when the judges declared it unsuitable, they had found the *Cycloped* had actually moved back a little rather than going forward.

2. **In which year did the original Eurostar terminal open at Waterloo?**

a) 1991

b) 1993

c) 1994

3. **The long-distance Amtrak route from Chicago to San Antonio is known as the "Texas ..."**

a) Flyer

b) Eagle

c) Star

4. **Which members of railway staff were nicknamed "bobbies"?**

a) Porters

b) Booking clerks

c) Signalmen

MYSTERY SUDOKU

Complete the grid so that every row, column and 3 × 3 box contains the letters EIKLNORTW in any order. One row or column contains a seven-letter word applicable to the railways. What is it?

	W		O			N		
R				T		L		O
K				I				
W	O	K						
	E						L	
						E	O	W
			L					K
I		E		W				R
		R			E		T	

DOWN WORD

Place a three-letter word in the spaces in each row to complete a six-letter word. When the grid is completed correctly, a new word in the shaded letters will be formed; this could be a singularly attractive way to travel. What is it?

			A	C	T
			U	N	D
			H	O	W
			N	A	C
			P	I	T
			I	A	C
			G	H	Y
			O	Y	S

151

CROSS OUT

Cross out all the letters that appear more than once. The letters that are left, reading from left to right and top to bottom, will spell out an essential part of the railways. What is it?

N	B	H	U	D	P	F	W
G	X	T	O	L	N	Z	Q
V	E	I	D	Y	S	M	G
Z	N	Q	N	X	L	U	F
I	R	Y	W	P	E	A	V
O	D	S	C	M	K	H	B

152

MAZE

Train journeys are not always straightforward, as with the following journey, which is full of twists and turns. Drive the train from the top to the bottom.

CRISS-CROSS: WARSHIP CLASS

The Western Region Diesel-Hydraulic "Warship" Class was introduced in 1958, with most of these locomotives named after Royal Navy vessels. Shunt each of the following into the grid:

4 letters
Zest
Zulu

5 letters
Glory
Rapid
Swift

6 letters
Active
Daring
Superb
Viking

7 letters
Bulldog
Centaur
Eclipse
Goliath
Panther

Pegasus
Spartan
Warrior
Zealous

8 letters
Ark Royal
Conquest
Hercules
Intrepid
Vigilant

9 letters
Strongbow
Tenacious

10 letters
Formidable
Relentless
Victorious

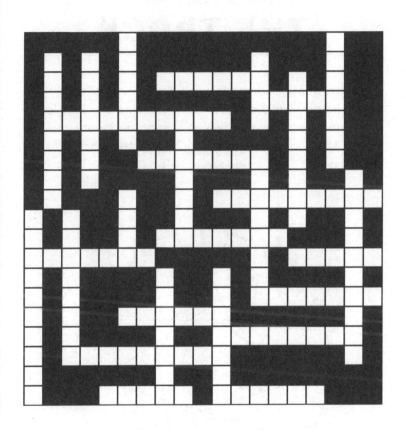

STAR OF
THE TRACK

The letters of the name of a well-known type of train have been spread evenly around the circle. Find the first letter in the name and follow the letters in order thereby making up the star – and this particular star of the track. What is the train?

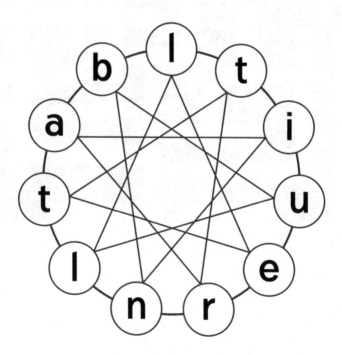

WORD LADDER

Something that needs to be continually checked and monitored on locomotives is the fuel tank. In this word ladder, fuel up the tank by changing one letter at a time to turn "fuel" into "tank".

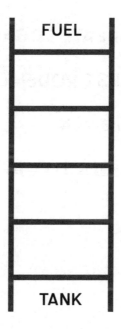

FUEL

TANK

ANAGRAMS

Unscramble the following to reveal the names of some stations on the London Underground. All these stations are found on which line?

1. THE ICY WIT

2. GREATEST CANAL

3. BEST RODENT

4. PIG PEN

5. NEWS TO CAT

LETTER DROP

The letters in each of the columns need to be entered into the squares immediately below, but not necessarily in the same order. By placing the letters in the correct squares you will reveal an interesting observation from the American writer Elisha Cooper.

	V		N	G		W			O	S		
M	H	L	I	T	G		R	H	W	O	D		H
A	O	M	A	R	L	E	T	N	R	L	R	L	D
T	S	E	A	L	R	A	I	O	R	I	U	G	A

WORD BUILDER

Something of interest to many railway users has been numbered one to nine. What is it?

Letters 1, 7 and 9 give us something expected

Letters 2, 8 and 4 give us a historic period

Letters 3, 9, 8 and 7 give us a South American country

Letters 6, 5, 4, 1 and 9 give us commerce

**Letters 7, 3, 1, 4, 6 and 2 give us the latest news
which could now be relevant**

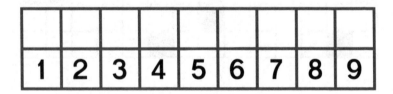

1	2	3	4	5	6	7	8	9

MINI SUDOKU: SAFETY

Safety is paramount on the railways and is also key here. Complete the grid so that every row, column and 2 × 3 box contains the letters that make up the word "safety".

	A		Y		T
		Y			
	F				S
F				E	
	Y		F		

WORD SEARCH: TRAINSPOTTER

There are many who enjoy trainspotting, but this time it is a case of finding the trainspotters in the train. There are two of them, but where are they?

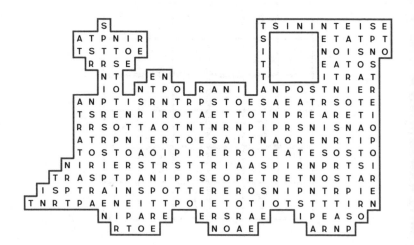

ACROSTICS

Solve the clues correctly and the shaded squares will reveal something familiar on the railways. What is it?

1. Harm
2. Challenge, call into question
3. Insect with pincers
4. Hunting expedition
5. XI
6. Small

1					
2					
3					
4					
5					
6					

TAKE YOUR PICK

Which of the following is the correct answer? Take your pick.

1. **In his painting *Rain, Steam and Speed*, British artist William Turner depicted a steam engine crossing which bridge designed by Isambard Kingdom Brunel?**
a) Maidenhead
b) Royal Albert Bridge
c) Windsor

2. **While working as a station master on the Newcastle & Carlisle Railway in the late 1830s, what did Thomas Edmondson devise?**
a) A station master's pocket watch, complete with chain
b) A standard whistle for use on stations
c) A card-type railway ticket

3. **Which station has the longest platform in Britain?**
a) Gloucester
b) Birmingham New Street
c) London Euston

4. **In 1972, the actor Lord Olivier mounted a campaign concerning changes to the breakfast menu on the Brighton Belle express train to London. What was it?**
a) To keep kippers on the menu.
b) To continue to offer full English breakfast rather than replace it with a Continental breakfast.
c) To continue to offer the choice of loose-leaf tea in teapots rather than just teabags.

WORD LINK

Each of the three words in the clues below have a word in common. For example, if the clues were "level", "seller" and "Sunday", the answer would be "best" ("level best", "best seller" and "Sunday best"). Answer each of the following clues correctly to reveal a word in the shaded column and something important and appreciated on the railways. What is it?

1. voice, down, knee
2. door, time, day
3. busy, guard, out
4. table, brain, game
5. wide, wound, secret
6. air, line, metal
7. last, code, office

1			
2			
3			
4			
5			
6			
7			

ON TRACK

Find the start, then moving one letter at a time – either horizontally, vertically or diagonally – discover something many train enthusiasts enjoy and appreciate. The answer is two words. What is it?

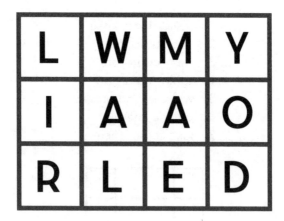

L	W	M	Y
I	A	A	O
R	L	E	D

STRANGE BUT TRUE

In 1911 how was William "Bumper" Harris usefully employed at Earls Court station?

1. In view of the growing instances of crime being reported at the station, ex-policeman William "Bumper" Harris was employed to stop the pickpockets and so reassure the travelling public of the safety of the station. On his first day at work Harris had his own wallet stolen, but quickly set to work and successfully apprehended over 30 pickpockets in his first week of employment.

2. He was a London busker and found that Earls Court station had particularly good acoustics. He approached the station authorities and was allowed to sing on the condition that part of his earnings was donated to a local orphanage. He was so successful he was allowed to busk at the station until the outbreak of war in 1914.

3. William "Bumper" Harris was a one-legged engineer, and considered a suitable candidate to demonstrate the safety of the new escalators at the station by riding up and down with ease.

4. He rid the station of nuisance pigeons. Harris was so effective he was offered similar work at other stations.

A PICTURE POSER

What essential requirement is suggested by the following?

MYSTERY SUDOKU

Complete the grid so that every row, column and 3 × 3 box contains the letters AEHILMNRT in any order. One row or column contains an eight-letter word and an important part of the railways. What is it?

I	H			N				
			E				R	A
R			A			T		
A	R			M				
		N				L		
				A			I	T
		M			A			E
H	A				T			
				I			L	H

WORD SEARCH: DEPOTS

Vital maintenance work is carried out in depots throughout the country. Find all the following depots within the depot opposite.

Allerton

Bournemouth

Chester

Clacton

Crewe

Dundee

East Ham

Fratton

Holyhead

Ilford

Inverness

Northam

Oxley

Penzance

Ryde

DOWN WORD

Place a three-letter word in the spaces in each row to complete a six-letter word. When the grid is completed correctly, a new word in the shaded letters will be formed, describing a problem that railway authorities have to sometimes deal with. What is it?

			L	U	S
			P	I	T
			S	I	T
			I	G	N
			X	E	S
			W	A	X
			E	C	T
			F	U	L

CODED CROSSWORD

In the grid below, each letter of the alphabet has been replaced by a number. To solve the puzzle, you must decide which letter is represented by which number. To help you start, one of the words has been partly filled in. When you have solved the code, complete the bottom grid to discover the motto of the London North Eastern Railway.

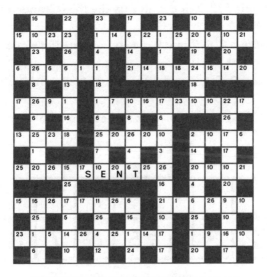

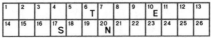

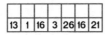

WORD BUILDER

The letters of something many a railway authority has to deal with have been numbered one to nine. Solve the clues to discover what it is.

Letters 8, 5, 3 and 4 give us some grit

Letters 9, 2, 7 and 3 give us the most important

Letters 8, 6, 7 and 9 give us something slender

Letters 2, 3, 1, 7 and 6 give us a blacksmith's block

Letters 1, 5, 6, 7 and 4 give us something legally acceptable

1	2	3	4	5	6	7	8	9

CRYPTOGRAM

Solve the cryptogram to discover a truism from the writer John Betjeman. To give you a start, Q = S, K = D and D = V.

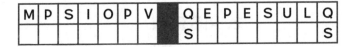

M	P	S	I	O	P	V		Q	E	P	E	S	U	L	Q
								S							S

P	M	R		F	U	Q	E		S	F	Y	U	M	E	P	L	E
						S											

S	L		B	S	D	S	L	B		Y	I	P	A	R	Q
					V										S

P	L		S	K	R	L	E	S	E	V
				D						

ANAGRAMS

Solve the anagrams to reveal some railway-related words.

1. CIGAR ERA

2. PISTON

3. LET WISH

4. IN DIGS

5. OPTED

STAR OF
THE TRACK

The letters of the name of a famous express have been spread evenly around the circle. Find the first letter in the name and follow the letters in order thereby making up the star – and this particularly striking star of the track. What is it?

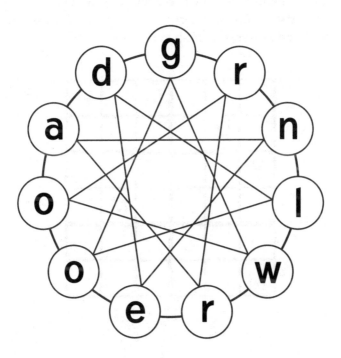

MINI SUDOKU: HYMEKS

Class 35 locomotives were developed for the Western region of British Rail and, because of their hydraulic Mekydro transmission, became known as Hymeks. One hundred and one were built between 1961 and 1964. In this mini sudoku, complete the grid so that every row, column and 2 × 3 box contains the letters that make up the name of these highly regarded and reliable diesel-hydraulic locomotives, "Hymeks".

			M		H
	H			E	
Y			S		
				M	
		E			
M	K				

HIDDEN NAMES

Hidden in each of the following sentences is the name of a major railway station in the UK. As an example, in the sentence "The station master looked over the platform," the hidden station is Dover (looke**d over**). What other station names lurk below?

1. Station officials became suspicious of the ticket holder by the kiosk.

2. The railway modeller eagerly set about recreating the station scene at home.

3. In view of the increased demand, the crew volunteered to give up rest on their day off.

4. The officials had to decide whether to delay or keep to a reduced service.

5. As the train was slow, I'd nestle down in my seat and tackle this puzzle in *The Train Lover's Puzzle Book*.

HIDDEN WORD

Fit the following words into the grid so that a new word is created in the shaded squares. This is something that the locomotive engineer Robert Weatherburn took much pride in. What was it?

BRIDGE
COACH
DELAYS
METRO
SHUNT
TICKET
TUNNEL

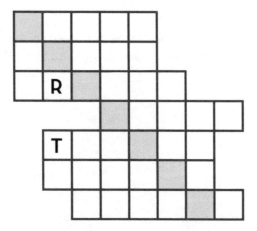

TRAIN TRACKS

Time to lay some tracks to link station A to station B. The numbers tell you how many sections of track go in each column and row. Only straight or curved rails can be used and the track cannot cross itself. Some pieces of the track have already been laid – now it is over to you.

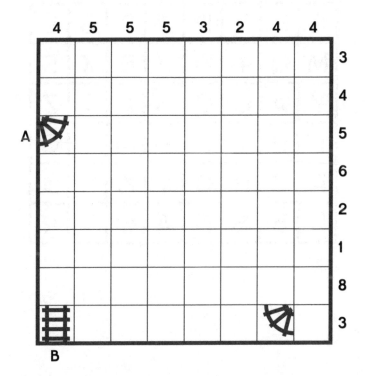

CROSS OUT

Cross out all the letters that appear more than once. The letters that are left, reading from left to right and top to bottom, will spell out something that helps ensure the safe running of the railways. What is it?

C	H	V	R	D	P	G	L
M	Q	I	W	U	B	X	F
Y	A	G	C	S	L	T	Z
L	U	X	P	F	M	I	G
P	Z	H	O	V	W	K	D
E	B	S	N	A	Q	Y	R

SAINTLY STATIONS

There are quite a few stations in the UK with "saint" in their name, but where are these stations situated? Match the station name to its location.

1. St Davids	a) Bedford
2. St Erth	b) Liverpool
3. St Margarets	c) Wolverhampton
4. St Michaels	d) Exeter
5. St Johns	e) Paisley
6. St Paul's (metro)	f) Cornwall
7. St George's (metro)	g) Birmingham
8. St James	h) Hertfordshire

ON TRACK

Find the start, then moving one letter at a time – either horizontally, vertically or diagonally – discover a word that has an interested connection. What is it?

R	R	E	T
T	A	P	T
I	N	S	O

TAKE YOUR PICK

Which of the following is the correct answer? Take your pick.

1. **In January 1964, Stamford Brook Underground station was chosen for the first what?**
a) First automated loud speaker announcement system.
b) First automatic ticket gates.
c) First station to have "Mind the Gap" painted on the platforms.

2. **American engineer Zerah Colburn wrote, "No innovation, in respect of locomotive engines, ever divided practical and professional opinion so completely." What was he referring to?**
a) Chimney
b) Drive rod
c) Valve gear

3. **On an InterCity express in the 1980s the buffet car steward announced that "only cold meat will be on the menu for dinner tonight". What reason was given?**
a) Two of the catering staff missed the train.
b) The buffet car was the wrong way around.
c) The sausages and burgers were still in Paddington.

4. **One of the most famous British railway posters of all time was by John Hassall showing a jolly sailor and advertising excursions to a seaside resort that "is so bracing". What was the seaside resort?**
a) Margate
b) Blackpool
c) Skegness

WORD SEARCH: CASTLES

The Collett 4 Cylinder 4-6-0's "Castle Class" are considered to be among the most famous of classes ever to run. In this word search track down the following locomotives, each named after a castle.

Barbury
Builth
Cardiff
Chirk
Corfe
Dorchester
Dunster
Harlech
Hereford
Highclere
Lulworth
Monmouth
Pembroke
Raglan
Swansea
Tenby
Totnes
Usk
Warwick
Windsor

```
R T A O X D R S A E S N A W S R G
S E K V W O E J E C M Q K G Z R Q
Y N U J S N B N R S A R Y M C P P
R B C D T O Z T E A I R S I H O E
C Y N O P W N O L H D E D E J X M
P I T D F A V Z C I Z U F I P I B
W C H T L I U B H Q C A N R F R R
S Q W O M H Q K G R R G J S O F O
V T Y A D Z P O I Y Y W N F T C K
F N R O R T F D H U W T Q I V E E
L E U C O W H T U O M N O M F B R
I X B R F R I D O R C H E S T E R
A W R P E A Y C L U L W O R T H K
R V A T R G T W K U X F L K R T Z
K W B Z E L F F F D X P U J M O W
Q S E C H A W U H C E L R A H V H
C A U Z L N M C V Y E E W K B I Y
```

WORD LINK

Each of the three words in the clues below have a word in common. For example, if the clues were "level", "seller" and "Sunday", the answer would be "best" ("level best", "best seller" and "Sunday best"). Answer each of the following clues correctly to reveal a word in the shaded column and something that has played an important part in the running and development of the railways. What is it?

1. mark, over, high
2. cloud, acid, gauge
3. off, step, quiet
4. out, mark, boarding
5. line, family, surgeon
6. pelt, stop, fare

1			
2			
3			
4			
5			
6			

TRIVIA

1. In which city is the National Railway Museum located?

2. In a mechanical signal box, what do white levers indicate?

3. What does the abbreviation APT stand for?

4. Situated in Kent and running since 1927, it is one of the world's smallest public railways. What is this railway called?

5. In which county is the Bluebell Railway?

6. Shrub Hill and Foregate Street stations are found in which city?

7. In September 2021 two new London Underground stations opened. Nine Elms and Battersea Power Station. On which line are they?

8. The TGV is France's intercity high-speed rail service. What are the letters TGV short for?

9. Until it was closed in 1969 the royal family frequently used Wolferton station as it was close to which royal estate?

10. What source of power is used for the Lynton & Lynmouth Cliff Railway?

CRISS-CROSS: JUBILEE CLASS

Many of Stanier's intermediate express class 3-cylinder 4-6-0s were named after places and countries. In this criss-cross find a place for all of the following:

4-letter name
Fiji

5-letter names
Assam
India
Kenya
Tonga

6-letter names
Bombay
Canada
Ceylon
Cyprus
Quebec
Tobago
Uganda

7-letter names
Bahamas
Jamaica
Kashmir
Nigeria
Ontario

8-letter names
Tasmania
Trinidad
Victoria
Zanzibar

9-letter names
Australia
Mauritius

10-letter names
New Zealand
Queensland

11-letter name
South Africa

12-letter name
Newfoundland

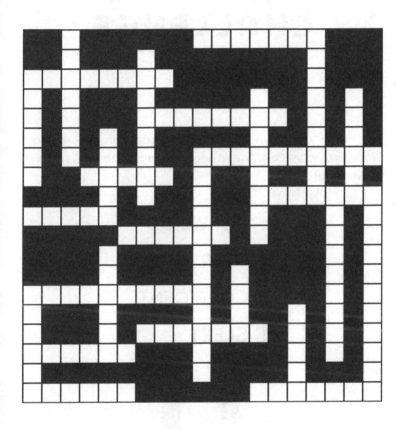

ANAGRAM CHALLENGE

PEERLESS

This is an anagram of something seen on the railway. Once you solve this, the other anagrams should be easier to work out.

1. NO! WE DO

2. STAR ICON

3. CORE CENT

4. SLEET

MYSTERY SUDOKU

Complete the grid so that every row, column and 3 × 3 box contains the letters AEIJLNORV in any order. One row or column contains a seven-letter name of a train. What is it?

E	R						O	
		V	N				L	A
					A			V
			N				R	
A			V		I			L
	N			J				
O			L					
N	A				J	E		
	E						I	R

WHAT THEY SAID

The following quotes have some of their words missing. What are they?

1. **Paul Theroux, in his celebrated book *The Old Patagonian Express*, wrote "One of the virtues of train travel is that …"**

a) You can think, write, talk, sleep or just do nothing.
b) You know where you are by looking out of the window.
c) It can take you on the most wondrous journeys.

2. **American railroad executive Alfred E. Perlman, considering the management of the railways, believed that "All it takes is common sense and …"**

a) Good timetabling.
b) Modern equipment.
c) Delivering service.

3. **In writing about railways, Rudyard Kipling advised, "Make the platform speak. …"**

a) It is the start of adventure.
b) It should have some tales to tell.
c) It is the place of beginnings and endings.

RAILWAY MERGER

Two railway-related words have been merged together. The letters are in the correct order and the words are of equal length. Can you separate the two words and determine what they are? As an example, in BRGAUAKRDE the words "guard" and "brake" have been merged together.

1. SPIOGINTNASL

2. BCOOGACIEH

3. RSATAITLIWOANY

4. TOIFCFKIECET

5. BTRUNIDNGELE

6. STTERAAIMN

MINI SUDOKU: MAGLEV

Maglev trains use magnetic levitation to move without touching the ground and, with no rail friction, are capable of reaching speeds of 373 mph. However, in this mini sudoku, speed is not of the essence as you can take your time to complete the grid so that every row, column and 2 × 3 box contains the letters that make up "maglev".

			A		
		L	M	V	
		G			E
		V		L	
	M				

192

CODED CROSSWORD

In the grid below, each letter of the alphabet has been replaced by a number. To solve the puzzle, you must decide which letter is represented by which number. To help you start, one of the words has been partly filled in. When you have solved the code, complete the bottom grid to discover an advertising slogan used by the Canadian National Railway.

4		17		23		19		18		23		16		14
14	9	12	5	14	23	22		23	17	17	18	24	7	19
10		22		18		5		1		8		22		17
19	22	24	25	22	5	2		2	25	17	21	10	8	22
10		14				17		24		13		25		17
23	24	9	4	13	24	25	20	19		17	15	23	14	2
				17				22		22		17		10
10	9	26	14	9	10	19		19	20	14	12	17	12	19
23		25		17		5				3				
10	6	5	24	23 (L)		12	25	24	20	10	4	25	5	13
8		13		14 (I)		17		11				14		24
22	14	2	19	22 (T)	10	25		24	26	10	23	17	9	26
25		14		7		4		23		15		22		23
14	22	10	13	14	19	10		10	3	14	23	10	1	10
8		25		8		25		24		22		4		3

1	2	3	4	5	6	7	8	9	10	11	12	13
14 (I)	15	16	17	18	19	20	21	22 (T)	23 (L)	24	25	26

| 8 | 17 | 5 | 25 | 22 | 10 | 19 | 1 | | 24 | 9 | 4 | | 19 | 10 | 25 | 3 | 14 | 8 | 10 |

WORD LADDER

Every autumn, thousands of tons of leaves fall on the railway causing delays and problems. If the leaves stick to the rails they can affect train braking and acceleration so, to prevent disruption, teams and leaf-busting trains are employed to keep tracks clear. In this word ladder, leaves present another challenge as you change one letter at a time to turn "leaf" into "fall".

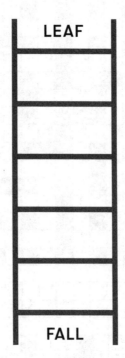

LEAF

FALL

LETTER DROP

The letters in each of the columns need to be entered into the squares immediately below, but not necessarily in the same order. By placing the letters in the correct squares you will reveal an interesting thought from the American professional basketball and television personality Charles Barkley.

						T		A		E			
	S		T	T	T		T	U	T	H	N		I
O	I	G	M	E	E	A	T	R	S	N	E	H	E	T	D
L	F	O	H	H	A	I	M	E	N	I	T	L	A	N	S

CRISS-CROSS: BRITISH RAILWAY COMPANIES

During the development of the railways, Britain has had over a thousand different railway companies. Some operated a few miles of track and some just a few hundred yards as they connected a town to a harbour or another link. Many of these companies became absorbed by larger ones but, in homage to these early companies and where they existed, find a place for each in the grid opposite.

3-letter name
Hay

4-letter names
Bala
Mold

5-letter names
Alloa
Barry
Calne
Chard

6-letter names
Bognor
Lanark
Moffat

Ramsey
Wirral

7-letter names
Forcett
Hunslet
Wenlock

8-letter names
Aberdare
Alcester
Coniston
Findhorn
Monkland
Monmouth

9-letter names
Cowbridge
Gravesend
Newmarket

10-letter names
Abbotsbury
Okehampton

11-letter names
Oystermouth
Stourbridge

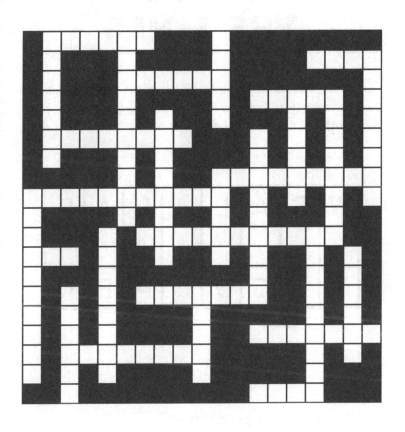

BETWEEN THE LINES

Something that is particularly valued about the railways can be inserted in the blank line so that, reading downwards, eight three-letter words are formed. What lies between the lines?

W	S	A	L	A	L	A	P
Y	T	C	D	E	P	E	N

ANAGRAMS

Unscramble the anagrams to reveal the names of famous engineers who contributed much to the development of the railways.

1. EGG ON THE RESPONSE

2. I THRIVED RICH TRACK

3. MAN'S DREAM — BUILDING BR, OK!

4. ELSE GINGERLY

5. LOVELIER BUILD

CRYPTOGRAM

Solve the cryptogram to discover an image described by Neil Somerville. To give you a start, J = D and W = M.

Q	I		Z		J	Y	O	X	O	C	J		E	D	Z	P	G	Q	F	W
					D						D									M

Z		P	Y	W	C	P	Z	L	D	C		Q	G		P	F	Z	Y	I	O
				M																

P	V	Z	P		S	Y	D	D		I	C	M	C	F		B	Q	W	C
																		M	

WORD LINK

This book has been a celebration of the railways, but in their building and running many have made great sacrifices and this puzzle is a tribute to those lost or who have suffered. In order to complete this puzzle, each of the three words in the clues below have a word in common. For example, if the clues were "level", "seller" and "Sunday", the answer would be "best" ("level best", "best seller" and "Sunday best"). Answer each of the following clues correctly to reveal an appropriate word in the shaded column as well as the name of a great locomotive. What is it?

1. face, time, money
2. fruit, witness, brown
3. sign, box, roll
4. play, game, offer
5. dust, mine, shovel
6. arts, print, feel
7. show, lunch, start

WORD BUILDER

Something seen at many railway stations has been numbered one to nine. What is it?

Letters 1, 4 and 5 give us hardly any

Letters 2, 8 and 6 give us some beer

Letters 9, 2, 7 and 4 give us an auction

Letters 8, 2, 9, 6 and 3 give us a beam

Letters 5, 2, 1, 4 and 3 give us a thin biscuit

1	**2**	**3**	**4**	**5**	**6**	**7**	**8**	**9**

ANSWERS

1. Anagrams

1 ticket machine, 2 barrier,
3 waiting room, 4 footbridge,
5 escalator

2. Mystery Sudoku

T	G	H	I	S	E	A	W	L
E	L	W	G	A	T	H	S	I
I	S	A	H	L	W	T	G	E
G	I	L	E	H	S	W	T	A
S	W	T	L	G	A	I	E	H
H	A	E	T	W	I	G	L	S
L	T	G	A	E	H	S	I	W
A	E	S	W	I	G	L	H	T
W	H	I	S	T	L	E	A	G

3. Railway Slang

1 b), 2 a), 3 c), 4 b)

4. Down Word

Ashore, alpaca, bedsit, meteor,
sparks, beetle, archer. The
important and necessary part of
the railways is "sleeper".

5. Word Search

The station revealed in the
remaining letters is South
Kensington.

6. Strange but True

2 As the train was not travelling
fast and the president fell on
sand being used to carry out
track repairs, luckily he suffered
no serious injury.

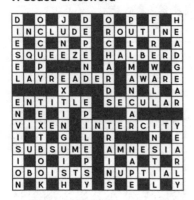

The famous train enthusiast was Czech composer Dvorak. His love of trains was so great he once noted, "I'd give all my symphonies if I could have invented the locomotive!"

8. What They Said
1 b), 2 a), 3 b)

9. On Track
Lost property

10. Trivia
1 Moscow and Helsinki, 2 Abraham Lincoln, 3 the Railway Cat, which is the subject of a poem by T. S. Eliot, 4 "Marrakesh Express", 5 Mornington Crescent, 6 Japanese bullet train, 7 pink, 8 4.50, 9 Brighton, 10 light, rapid, comfortable

11. Word Ladder
One possible solution: main, lain, laid, land, lane, line

12. Cross Out
Rack

13. Mini Sudoku: Deltic

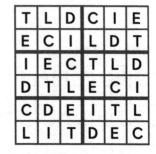

14. Word Builder
Passenger

15. A Riddle
Track

16. Crossword

The name of the famous express train was *Mallard*.

17. Letter Drop

Many times the wrong train took me to the right place.

18. Word Link

1 baby, 2 blue, 3 left, 4 soft, 5 free, 6 work. The word in the shaded column is "buffer".

19. Mystery Sudoku

R	D	L	S	T	A	P	E	O
O	E	A	P	R	D	S	T	L
S	T	P	O	E	L	D	R	A
T	A	S	L	P	E	O	D	R
L	O	R	A	D	S	E	P	T
D	P	E	R	O	T	A	L	S
E	S	D	T	A	R	L	O	P
P	L	T	D	S	O	R	A	E
A	R	O	E	L	P	T	S	D

Adlestrop is the name of the station immortalized in a poem by Edward Thomas. His train stopped at the station.

20. Take Your Pick

1 c), 2 a), 3 c), 4 c)

21. Fitting Words

The words need to be entered in the following order: siding, livery, bogie, shunt, steam and diesel. The word in the shaded squares is "signal".

22. Cryptogram

The most nearly perfect way of moving from one place to another.

23. Criss-Cross: Fishkind Wagons

24. Train Tracks

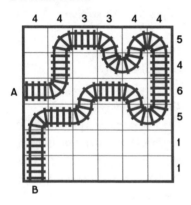

25. A Perplexing Poser

Noise

26. Star of the Track

Eurostar

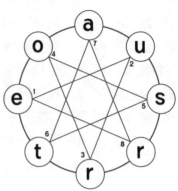

27. Strange but True

2 The ticket office was in a hollowed-out oak tree that had a circumference of 19 m.

28. Mini Sudoku: Subway

S	Y	U	B	A	W
B	W	A	S	U	Y
W	U	S	Y	B	A
Y	A	B	W	S	U
U	B	Y	A	W	S
A	S	W	U	Y	B

29. Letter Drop

"Isn't this invigorating?"
"No, sir, it's Croydon."

30. Word Builder
Buffet car

31. Word Ladder
One possible solution: live, line, lane, land, laid, raid, rail

32. On Track
Rolling stock

33. Railway Slang
1 c), 2 a), 3 a), 4 b)

34. Mystery Sudoku

O	D	N	I	G	R	S	A	E
G	A	I	S	N	E	R	O	D
E	S	R	O	D	A	N	I	G
I	E	G	A	S	D	O	R	N
N	O	D	E	R	I	G	S	A
A	R	S	G	O	N	E	D	I
S	I	O	N	A	G	D	E	R
D	G	A	R	E	O	I	N	S
R	N	E	D	I	S	A	G	O

35. Mystery Location
1 strong, 2 infer, 3 cafe, 4 knit, 5 beacon, 6 other. The mystery location, which appears in two of the down columns, is "ticket office".

36. Cross Out
Bogie

37. What They Said
1 c), 2 c), 3 c)

38. Criss-Cross: London Underground

39. Letter Drop
How does one train hear that another one's coming? With its engine-ears.

40. Maze

42. Mystery Sudoku

A	V	R	G	Y	T	M	E	O
M	T	G	O	E	R	Y	V	A
O	Y	E	M	V	A	T	R	G
Y	M	O	V	A	G	E	T	R
R	A	V	E	T	O	G	Y	M
G	E	T	R	M	Y	O	A	V
T	R	M	Y	O	V	A	G	E
V	O	Y	A	G	E	R	M	T
E	G	A	T	R	M	V	O	Y

The British Rail Class 220 Voyager is a class of diesel-electric high-speed multiple-unit passenger train operated by CrossCountry.

41. Take Your Pick

1 b), 2 a), 3 b) (Queen Victoria refused to allow her train to travel more than 40 mph in daylight hours or 30 mph at night), 4 a)

43. A Picture Poser

Wooden sleepers (wood den sleep purse)

44. Anagrams

1 level crossing, 2 engine shed, 3 signal box, 4 viaduct, 5 goods yard

45. Cryptogram

There was no doubt in my mind that steam engines all had definite personalities.

46. Word Ladder

One possible solution: well, tell, tall, talk, tank

47. Strange but True

3

48. (S)team Follower

Liverpool, Arsenal, Everton, Leicester City, West Ham United

49. Train Tracks

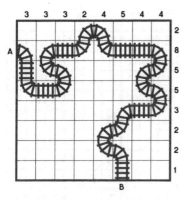

50. Coded Crossword

A performing dog was once handed in to a lost property office and entertained staff by walking around on its hind legs.

51. A Riddle

Gauge

52. Word Quest: Train

Air, ani, ant, anti, art, nit, rain, ran, rani, rant, rat, tan, tar, tarn, tin

53. Code Breaker

1 d), 2 a), 3 f), 4 e), 5 b), 6 c)

54. Word Builder

Nameplate

55. Mini Sudoku: Boiler

56. Star of the Track
The Rocket

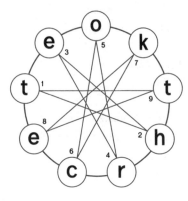

57. Word Search: Paris Metro

The hidden station is Bastille.

58. Letter Drop
What will ever equal the action of rods and valve gear flashing in the sunlight?

59. Take Your Pick
1 c), 2 b), 3 b), 4 b) (the trains have been nicknamed *Le Petit Train Jaune*)

60. Word Ladder
One possible solution: peak, pear, hear, hoar, hour

61. Mystery Sudoku

E	D	R	F	T	M	H	I	G
H	G	T	D	I	R	M	E	F
I	M	F	E	H	G	R	D	T
F	R	E	I	G	H	T	M	D
G	T	D	M	F	E	I	H	R
M	I	H	T	R	D	G	F	E
D	E	I	G	M	T	F	R	H
R	F	G	H	E	I	D	T	M
T	H	M	R	D	F	E	G	I

62. What They Said
1 c), 2 c) (the reason Oscar Wilde gave was because "One should always have something sensational to read in the train"), 3 a)

63. Fitting Words
When the words disturb, younger, Niagara, artwork, Marconi, insulin and closing are entered in that order, the words "dynamic braking" will appear in the shaded squares.

64. Station Codes

1 Guildford, 2 Wimbledon,
3 Southampton, 4 Norwich,
5 Leeds, 6 Brighton,
7 Cambridge, 8 Sheffield,
9 Northampton, 10 Barrow-in-Furness

65. Strange but True

2

66. Railway Slang

1 b), 2 c), 3 a), 4 c)

67. Hidden Names

1 Swindon, 2 Hereford, 3 Reading,
4 Crewe, 5 Stoke

68. At the Junction

Ticket machine

69. Cross Out

Wagon

70. A Riddle

Route

71. Word Ladder

One possible solution: mile, pile,
pole, pose, post

72. Take Your Pick

1 b), 2 c) (Brunel considered it
"impossible" that a man who
indulged in reading should make
a good engine-driver as, being
a thinker and without "anything
to attract" their attention, they
are likely to begin "thinking
of something else" and not
concentrate on the job in hand),
3 a), 4 a)

73. Train Tracks

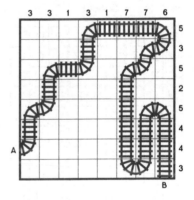

74. Cryptogram

In the shed
An old engine
Lovingly restored

75. Criss-Cross: Model Railways

76. Mystery Sudoku

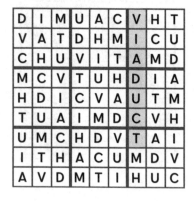

D	I	M	U	A	C	V	H	T
V	A	T	D	H	M	I	C	U
C	H	U	V	I	T	A	M	D
M	C	V	T	U	H	D	I	A
H	D	I	C	V	A	U	T	M
T	U	A	I	M	D	C	V	H
U	M	C	H	D	V	T	A	I
I	T	H	A	C	U	M	D	V
A	V	D	M	T	I	H	U	C

77. Word Builder

Footplate

78. Word Search: Locomotives

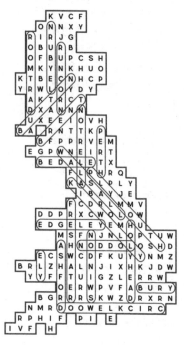

79. Anagrams

1 cleaner, 2 inspector, 3 station manager, 4 train driver, 5 signalman

80. Acrostics

1 shunt, 2 ennui, 3 attic, 4 speak, 5 olive, 6 night. The words in the shaded squares are "season ticket".

81. Coded Crossword

The culprits were **crows**. These birds liked the yellow grease that filled the axle boxes on the goods wagons. When the wagons were taken out of the sidings, sparks were seen coming from some of the axle boxes and, on investigation, it was found that crows had eaten the grease!

82. Maze

83. Letter Drop

Now we have perfection found
The bright electric Underground

84. Take Your Pick

1 b), 2 a), 3 c), 4 b)

85. Word Search: Expresses

The express named in the remaining squares is *Brighton Belle*.

86. Mini Sudoku: Poster

E	S	P	R	O	T
R	T	O	P	S	E
O	R	E	S	T	P
S	P	T	O	E	R
P	E	S	T	R	O
T	O	R	E	P	S

87. Fitting Words

When the words are entered in the following order – track, depot, van, bridge, brakes, driver – the word "tender" appears in the shaded squares.

88. Between the Lines

Ebb, bad, fly, old, ram, asp, sty. The word between the lines is "ballast".

89. What They Said

1 c), 2 a), 3 b)

90. On Track

Penalty fares

91. Trivia

1 Bournemouth West (from 1965 to 1967 it was extended to Poole), 2 Hampstead, 3 Georgia, 4 Chicago, 5 the service between Bedford and St Pancras, 6 George Bradshaw, 7 Waterloo, 8 rail-fastening, 9 overhead line, 10 the Docklands Light Railway

92. Cryptogram

Slow train travel is almost the only restful experience that is left to us. I love it.

93. Word Search: Lost Railway

```
R I A W R A I Y W A R I A R Y
W R I Y L R Y I W R A I R A R
A A L R A W R R L R I R A R I
R L A Y R Y I A R A L Y R Y L
A I R W I W R W Y L W R L A R
R A I A R A L Y R A Y L A R W
I L W R L Y I Y I R A W I A R
A R I Y A R W A R Y L R A I Y
W A R R L A I R A I R Y R A R
L R I W R I W A Y I W A Y W A
R L I A R L W L R A I L A R W
R A Y A W Y I A R L A W L A R
Y R A L A R R Y W I L A Y R A
A I W R I A Y A Y I R Y I W R
R A I A L W Y L I R A I Y R I
```

94. Word Ladder

One possible solution: sub, pub, pun, pan, pay, way

95. Anagrams

1 St Pancras, 2 Fenchurch Street, 3 London Bridge, 4 Liverpool Street, 5 Euston

96. Word Builder

Pendolino. This electric high-speed tilting train is used in many countries and in the UK (British Rail Class 390) is operated by Avanti West Coast.

97. Hidden Names

1 George, 2 Percy, 3 Peter, 4 Eric, 5 Clive

98. Railway Slang

1 b), 2 c), 3 a), 4 a)

99. Mystery Sudoku

E	R	F	H	M	U	O	N	I
U	N	I	F	O	R	M	H	E
O	H	M	I	N	E	F	U	R
I	E	N	U	F	O	H	R	M
H	O	U	N	R	M	E	I	F
F	M	R	E	I	H	U	O	N
R	F	O	M	U	I	N	E	H
N	U	H	R	E	F	I	M	O
M	I	E	O	H	N	R	F	U

100. Criss-Cross: Amtrak Routes

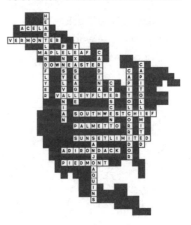

101. Word Link

1 fast, 2 slip, 3 made, 4 main, 5 many, 6 high. The word in the shaded column is "siding".

102. Letter Drop
Nowhere can I think so happily as in a train.

103. Train Tracks

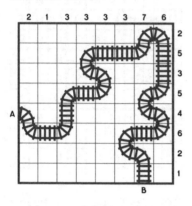

104. Star of the Track
Puffing Billy, the world's oldest surviving steam locomotive.

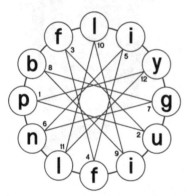

105. Mind the Gap
Carriage

106. Strange but True
2 The subway cars were cleaned, with as much removed and recycled as possible. The cars were then dropped at sea becoming artificial reefs and a valuable new habitat for marine life.

107. Mini Sudoku: Signal

G	A	N	I	S	L
I	L	S	G	A	N
L	G	A	S	N	I
S	N	I	A	L	G
A	I	L	N	G	S
N	S	G	L	I	A

108. Acrostics
1 start, 2 tutor, 3 extra, 4 alibi, 5 melon. The something of interest that appears in the shaded squares is "steam train".

109. A Perplexing Poser
Timetable

110. Word Quest: Railway
Ail, air, airway, airy, alar, alary, aria, aril, aryl, away, awl, awry, lair, lairy, law, lay, liar, lira, rail, raw, rawly, ray, ria, rial, riyal, wail, war, warily, wary, way, wily, wiry, wry, yaw, yawl

111. On Track
Waiting rooms

112. Take Your Pick
1 a), 2 c) (in order to catch a train, passengers had to take the Dartmouth Passenger Ferry across the Dart estuary to Kingswear railway station), 3 a), 4 b) (the meandering routes on a map resembled the branches of a sickly tree, hence the name. Sir John Betjeman called it "the most exciting train journey I know").

113. Word Search: At the Station

114. Anagrams
1 *The Flying Scotsman*, 2 *Orient Express*, 3 *Eurostar*, 4 *Enterprise*, 5 *Golden Arrow*

115. What They Said
1 c), 2 a), 3 b)

116. Mystery Sudoku

N	I	A	O	E	H	S	L	D
O	H	S	A	D	L	E	I	N
D	E	L	I	N	S	H	O	A
E	A	D	L	H	O	N	S	I
L	N	O	S	I	E	A	D	H
H	S	I	D	A	N	L	E	O
S	L	N	H	O	D	I	A	E
A	D	H	E	S	I	O	N	L
I	O	E	N	L	A	D	H	S

This is the grip between the wheels of a train and rails of a track.

117. Word Ladder
One possible solution: head, held, hold, hole, home, come, code

118. Cross Out
Horn

119. A Riddle
Depot

120. Acrostics
1 siding, 2 iguana, 3 garden, 4 nugget, 5 anchor, 6 luxury. The words in the shaded columns are "signal gantry".

121. Strange but True

4 The "life" season ticket was sent with compliments from the Underground head office.

122. Word Builder

High speed

123. Word Link

1 draw, 2 near, 3 open, 4 cash, 5 gift, 6 drop, 7 used. The word in the shaded column is "repairs".

124. Letter Drop

Railway termini are our gates to the glorious and the unknown.

125. A Perplexing Poser

It was Jim. The only one who told the truth was Susie.

126. Mini Sudoku: Livery

V	L	R	E	I	Y
E	Y	I	R	V	L
I	E	L	V	Y	R
R	V	Y	I	L	E
L	R	V	Y	E	I
Y	I	E	L	R	V

127. Star of the Track

Orient Express

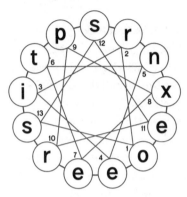

128. Hidden Names

1 Mona, 2 Gwen, 3 Vera, 4 Lydia, 5 Agatha

129. Take Your Pick

1 c), 2 a), 3 c), 4 c)

130. On Track

Station clock

131. Mystery Sudoku

U	I	T	S	D	M	A	O	R
D	A	S	I	O	R	U	T	M
R	M	O	A	T	U	D	S	I
O	T	I	U	S	A	R	M	D
S	R	A	D	M	I	O	U	T
M	U	D	T	R	O	I	A	S
I	D	M	O	A	T	S	R	U
T	O	U	R	I	S	M	D	A
A	S	R	M	U	D	T	I	O

132. Anagrams

1 Edinburgh Waverley, 2 Glasgow Central, 3 Cardiff Central, 4 Bristol Temple Meads, 5 Exeter St Davids

133. Railway Slang

1 b), 2 c), 3 b), 4 a)

134. Word Search: London Underground

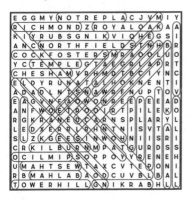

135. Word Ladder

One possible solution (without breaking any rules) is: rule, role, roll, toll, tool, took, book

136. Train Tracks

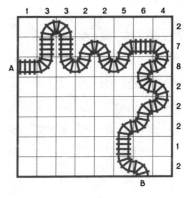

137. Down Word

Actual, potato, impugn, ampler, nutmeg, stymie, bedlam, arcade. The word in the shaded column is "commuter".

138. Railway Lines

1 e), 2 a), 3 j), 4 g), 5 b), 6 i), 7 c), 8 f), 9 h), 10 d)

139. X Marks the Spot

The words need to be entered in the following order: elephant, outdated, sorcerer, becoming, advisory, canister, calendar, listener. The mystery place in the shaded squares is "Eurostar terminal".

140. Cryptogram

The railway lover counts no time wasted which he spends sauntering on a good station.

141. Crossword

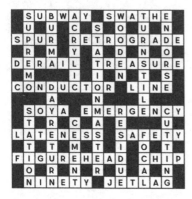

The famous train revealed in the shaded squares is the *Blue Train*, which operates in South Africa and is one of the most luxurious train journeys in the world.

142. Between the Lines

Ask, met, act, fun, era, rib, sty, dye. The word between the lines is "security".

143. Mini Sudoku: Points

P	O	N	T	S	I
I	S	T	N	O	P
T	I	S	O	P	N
N	P	O	S	I	T
S	N	P	I	T	O
O	T	I	P	N	S

144. Trivia

1 London Paddington and Plymouth, 2 general utility van, 3 a person who studies trains, 4 *Mallard*, 5 District. It has 60 stations, 6 The Liverpool Overhead Railway, 7 Charles Dickens, 8 Platform 9¾ King's Cross, 9 Isle of Wight, 10 between Adelaide and Darwin in Australia

145. Strange but True

2 James Wide lost both his legs in a railway accident. Following this he became a signalman and trained Jack, a baboon, to push his wheelchair as well as operate the railway signals under strict supervision. When word got out, the railway authorities checked Jack's competence and were so impressed the baboon was officially employed, being paid 20 cents a day and half a bottle of beer. Jack was employed for nine years and never made a mistake.

146. Word Search

N	U	E	E	L	A	H	C	S	E	A
W	D	G	O	D	S	H	I	L	L	L
O	S	D	T	Y	E	H	S	A	O	V
D	F	I	S	H	B	O	U	R	N	E
N	V	R	W	E	I	V	A	E	S	R
A	E	B	D	N	A	L	T	O	T	S
S	N	M	E	R	S	T	O	N	E	T
N	T	E	E	S	S	E	W	O	C	O
I	N	B	R	A	D	I	N	G	N	N
B	O	N	C	H	U	R	C	H	S	E
T	R	O	P	W	E	N	T	E	A	D

When the train crews were prohibited from using coal they "used stones instead".

147. On the Right Track

Platform announcement

148. Take Your Pick

1 a), 2 c), 3 b), 4 c) ("Bobby" is British slang for policemen, and the first signalmen were originally called "railway policemen", recruited to police the railway and regulate rail traffic).

149. Mystery Sudoku

E	W	L	O	R	K	N	I	T
R	I	N	E	T	W	L	K	O
K	T	O	N	I	L	R	W	E
W	O	K	L	E	I	T	R	N
N	E	T	W	O	R	K	L	I
L	R	I	T	K	N	E	O	W
T	N	W	R	L	O	I	E	K
I	L	E	K	W	T	O	N	R
O	K	R	I	N	E	W	T	L

150. Down Word

Impact, rotund, anyhow, cognac, armpit, maniac, dinghy, alloys. The shaded word is "monorail".

151. Cross Out

Track

152. Maze

153. Criss-Cross: Warship Class

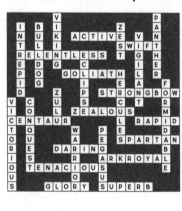

154. Star of the Track

Bullet train

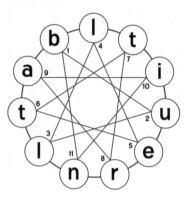

155. Word Ladder

One possible solution: fuel, full, fall, tall, talk, tank

156. Anagrams

1 White City, 2 Lancaster Gate, 3 Bond Street, 4 Epping, 5 West Acton. All these stations are on the Central Line.

157. Letter Drop

The train is a small world moving through a larger world.

158. Word Builder

Departure

159. Mini Sudoku: Safety

E	A	S	Y	F	T
Y	T	F	S	A	E
S	E	Y	A	T	F
A	F	T	E	Y	S
F	S	A	T	E	Y
T	Y	E	F	S	A

160. Word Search: Trainspotter

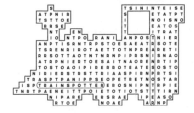

161. Acrostics

1 damage, 2 impugn, 3 earwig, 4 safari, 5 eleven, 6 little. The words in the shaded columns spell "diesel engine".

162. Take Your Pick

1 a), 2 c), 3 a), 4 a) (Lord Olivier won his battle to keep kippers on the menu and when the decision was announced he joked, "I think we'll have scrambled eggs this morning").

163. Word Link

1 deep, 2 next, 3 kept, 4 bird, 5 open, 6 base, 7 post. The word in the shaded column is "express".

164. On Track

Model railway

165. Strange but True

3 As well as being an engineer, William "Bumper" Harris only had one leg and was hired to ride up and down on the newly installed escalators to show how safe and easy they were to use. As a lot of the travelling public were unfamiliar with escalators, many had been terrified to use them until "Bumper" Harris was able to offer reassurance.

166. A Picture Poser

Track maintenance (track mane ten-ants)

167. Mystery Sudoku

I	H	A	T	N	R	E	M	L
M	T	L	E	H	I	N	R	A
R	N	E	A	L	M	T	H	I
A	R	T	I	M	L	H	E	N
E	I	N	R	T	H	L	A	M
L	M	H	N	A	E	R	I	T
N	L	M	H	R	A	I	T	E
H	A	I	L	E	T	M	N	R
T	E	R	M	I	N	A	L	H

168. Word Search: Depots

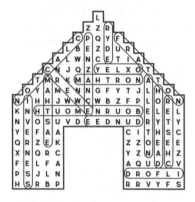

169. Down Word

Stylus, armpit, bedsit, assign, apexes, earwax, aspect, useful. The word in the shaded column is "trespass".

170. Coded Crossword

	R		P		L		S		L		E		M	
B	E	L	L		O	U	T	P	O	I	N	T	E	D
	L		A		C		U		O		Z		N	
T	A	T	T	O	O		D	U	M	M	Y	R	U	N
	X		F		M				M					
S	A	G	O		O	V	E	R	S	L	E	E	P	S
	T		R		T		X		T				A	
F	I	L	M		I	N	A	N	E		J	E	S	T
	O				V		C		W		U		S	
I	N	A	B	S	E	N	T	I	A		N	E	E	D
			I						R		C		N	
B	R	A	S	S	H	A	T		D	O	T	A	G	E
	I		Q		A		R		E		I		E	
L	O	Q	U	A	C	I	O	U	S		O	G	R	E
	T		E		K		Y		S		N		S	

The motto: "Forward".

171. Word Builder

Vandalism

172. Cryptogram

Railway stations are most important in giving places an identity.

173. Anagrams

1 carriage, 2 points, 3 whistle, 4 siding, 5 depot

174. Star of the Track

Golden Arrow

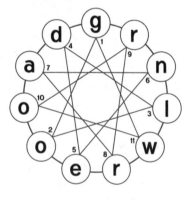

175. Mini Sudoku: Hymeks

E	Y	K	M	S	H
S	H	M	Y	E	K
Y	M	H	S	K	E
K	E	S	H	M	Y
H	S	E	K	Y	M
M	K	Y	E	H	S

176. Hidden Names
1 Derby, 2 Neath, 3 Preston,
4 York, 5 Widnes

177. Hidden Word
When the words are entered
in the following order – coach,
shunt, bridge, metro, tunnel,
ticket, delays – the word
"chimney" is created in the
shaded squares. Robert
Weatherburn considered
this especially important:
"Remember, as the hat is to
a well-dressed man, so is the
chimney to the locomotive."

178. Train Tracks

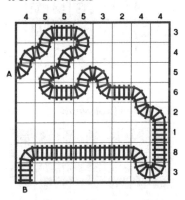

179. Cross Out
Token. This is a physical object
given to a train driver to
authorize use of a particular
stretch of single line.

180. Saintly Stations
1 d), 2 f), 3 h), 4 b), 5 a), 6 g), 7 c),
8 e)

181. On Track
Trainspotter

182. Take Your Pick
1 b), 2 c), 3 b), 4 c)

183. Word Search: Castles

184. Word Link
1 tide, 2 rain, 3 keep, 4 pass,
5 tree, 6 full. The word in the
shaded column is "diesel".

185. Trivia
1 York, 2 that they are spare
or unused levers, 3 advanced
passenger train, 4 Romney,
Hythe and Dymchurch Railway,
5 Sussex, 6 Worcester, 7 Northern,
8 *train à grande vitesse*,
9 Sandringham, 10 water

186. Criss-Cross: Jubilee Class

British Rail Class 395, a dual-voltage electric multiple unit built by Hitachi.

189. What They Said

1 b), 2 b), 3 b)

190. Railway Merger

1 points signal, 2 bogie coach,
3 railway station, 4 ticket office,
5 bridge tunnel, 6 steam train

191. Mini Sudoku: Maglev

V	G	M	A	E	L
A	E	L	M	V	G
M	V	G	L	A	E
E	L	A	G	M	V
G	A	V	E	L	M
L	M	E	V	G	A

187. Anagram Challenge

"Peerless" is an anagram of "sleepers" and the other anagrams are different classifications of railway sleepers, based on the material used. 1 wooden, 2 cast iron, 3 concrete, 4 steel.

188. Mystery Sudoku

E	R	A	I	L	V	N	O	J
J	O	V	N	E	R	I	L	A
I	L	N	J	O	A	R	E	V
L	V	I	A	N	O	J	R	E
A	J	E	V	R	I	O	N	L
R	N	O	E	J	L	V	A	I
O	I	R	L	V	E	A	J	N
N	A	L	R	I	J	E	V	O
V	E	J	O	A	N	L	I	R

192. Coded Crossword

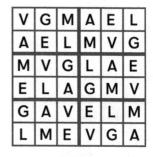

The advertising slogan used by Canadian National Railway is "Courtesy and Service".

193. Word Ladder
One possible solution: leaf, leap, heap, help, hell, fell, fall

194. Letter Drop
Sometimes that light at the end of the tunnel is a train.

195. Criss-Cross: British Railway Companies

196. Between the Lines
Why, set, arc, lid, ate, lap, age, pen. The word between the lines is "heritage".

197. Anagrams
1 George Stephenson, 2 Richard Trevithick, 3 Isambard Kingdom Brunel, 4 Nigel Gresley, 5 Oliver Bulleid

198. Cryptogram
On a disused platform
a timetable of trains
that will never come.

199. Word Link
1 save, 2 bear, 3 call, 4 fair, 5 coal, 6 fine, 7 late. The word in the shaded column is "Valiant" and is appropriate for those who have given so much to the railways as well as being the name of BR Co-Co Class 50 50015, currently a popular attraction on the heritage line run by the East Lancashire Railway.

200. Word Builder
The answer to this last puzzle is appropriately "farewells".

ACKNOWLEDGEMENTS

Writing and compiling *The Train Lover's Puzzle Book* has been great fun and, as always, I have been grateful for the support and interest of my family Ros, Richard and Emily.

Michael Beasley has been especially helpful with his encyclopaedic knowledge of railways and, dare I say, kept me on the right track. Thanks too to David Finnerty for his technical expertise.

As always it was a delight to work with my publisher Summersdale and particular thanks to my thorough and attentive editors Robert Drew and Chris Turton. I am also grateful to Emily Kearns for her excellent advice, and to Derek Donnelly for his meticulous proofread.

Also, in my research and reading, I began to appreciate more than ever the huge effort it has taken to build and run the railways, and I would like to acknowledge all those who have made the railways what they are – thank you. And thank you too for your interest in this book – it is appreciated.

ABOUT THE
AUTHOR

One of **Neil Somerville**'s earliest memories was standing with his parents on a platform. As an express was about to pass through the station, he was taken to the waiting room for safety. To this day, Neil remembers looking out and watching in awe as this huge train sped past. From that moment, his liking and respect of trains was born and since then he has enjoyed train travel in many countries as well as cycled and explored numerous disused lines.

When not out and about, Neil is a busy writer and puzzle setter. Over the years he has written many bestsellers, including *The Cycling Puzzle Book*, *For the Love of Radio 4: The Unofficial Puzzle Book*, *For the Love of The Archers: The Unofficial Puzzle Book* and *Cat Wisdom: 60 Great Lessons You Can Learn from a Cat*. He has also written a long series on Chinese horoscopes and contributes to many magazines and newspapers.

Neil lives in Berkshire with his wife and has two adult children. His website is www.neilsomerville.com.

THE
GARDENING
PUZZLE BOOK

200 BRAIN-TEASING
ACTIVITIES

FELICITY HART

THE GARDENING PUZZLE BOOK

200 Brain-Teasing Activities, from Crosswords to Quizzes

Felicity Hart

Hardback
978-1-80007-172-8
£12.99

This bountiful crop of 200 gardening-themed puzzles has something for anyone with green fingers and a love of a good brain-teaser.

Gardeners are a naturally smart species. But you don't need to be an expert to enjoy this book. When your hands deserve a rest after you've been out toiling in the garden, or when the weather has you cooped up inside, how about a puzzle or two to cultivate the mind? From quick quizzes and riddles to more leisurely crosswords and sudoku, whether you're a gardening obsessive or just enjoy pottering around your plot, there's plenty in these pages to tickle your fancy and keep your brain as sharp as a thorn and as strong as an oak.

Inside you will find a rich variety of puzzles, including these:

- Find the flowers, fruit and veg hiding within word searches
- Spot the differences between various idyllic views of a garden
- Shuffle the letters of anagrams to locate your trusty tools
- Wind your way through a series of intricate hedge mazes

Have you enjoyed this book? If so, find us on Facebook at **Summersdale Publishers**, on Twitter at **@Summersdale** and on Instagram at **@summersdalebooks** and get in touch. We'd love to hear from you!

www.summersdale.com